A Second Chance at Life

Personal Heart and Lung Transplant Stories

Freeman Hospital, Newcastle-upon-Tyne

Since 1985, over 2000 heart and lung transplants have been carried out on adults and children by the Freeman Hospital, Newcastle-upon-Tyne, England.*

* http://www.fhlta.org.uk/about/

© 2015

Published by Freeman Heart and Lung Transplant Association
www.fhlta.org.uk

First published 2015 by Freeman Heart and Lung Transplant Association

British Library Cataloguing in Publication Data
A catalogue record for this book is available from the British Library

Cover design by David Exley
Typesetting, Printing and Binding by Beamreach (www.beamreachuk.co.uk)

A Second Chance at Life

Personal Heart and Lung Transplant Stories

Edited by Judith Caulkin
and her son, Dr Richard Caulkin

Contents

Contents (cont.)

Contents (cont.)

This Book is Dedicated to:

All donors and their families everywhere for their unerring compassion to mankind.

This book would not have been able to be written by all The Freeman Hospital transplant survivors, who wished to be part of this celebration of their lives, if not for their donors who live on in these wonderful, proud human beings who live life to the full.

This Dedication is also to:

All the brave patients for who time runs out; for all who need a transplant at the end stage of their lives, which sadly doesn't happen in time.

For all who lose their lives as they become far too ill for a transplant to have been a life line for them.

How this book began ...

I thought of putting stories of Freeman transplant patients together in a book around the time when a young man I knew, called Gerard Falsey, who'd had a transplant, died. Around the same time I read 'Wendy's Story' on The FHLTA website. The aim of my idea would be to highlight the need for more people to join The Organ Donor Register.

Combined with my son's own experiences, Gerard's young life being lost and then reading of Wendy's years of suffering caused by heart problems, trying to cope with the hand she had been dealt, upset me so much, I felt the need to appeal to people who aren't affected by the world of transplantation, to put it out there; what better way than reading true-life stories and tributes of patient's experiences.

The other aspect of putting all the stories together is for other patients to read about each other's lives, as when we meet new recipients, we are always left with the feeling of the rightness of it all and I could listen to them all day long.

When I spoke to Wendy (Lingham) about the idea at The British Transplant Games in Bolton in August 2014, she agreed wholeheartedly to my using her story and thought it a good idea to produce a book. The next step was to ask Vicky Pettersen if she could put me in touch with Freeman patients; as a member of FHLTA Committee Vicky has access to all the patients' names and contact details. I wasn't allowed to get in touch with them but once word was out, they then contacted me.

It just snowballed from there on in, word of mouth, Facebook and emails daily to and fro.

I didn't need to ask twice for my son, Richard to take it all on board, he has helped enormously.

I learn new things every day about transplants. We never imagined half of what we know now following my son's illness, deterioration and finally his successful transplant and, given the opportunity, I know I would have welcomed reading first-hand what things could be like, how patients cope.

The reality is that not everyone gets the happy ending but the heartrending write-ups of this side of things just brings my philosophy to the fore; live for today and love every minute of your life.

I hope you enjoy reading this book as much as I have enjoyed editing it, even though sometimes I haven't been able to see for the tears it brings. It is a testament to so many brave people; the donors, their families and all the recipients of heart, lungs or heart & lung transplants belonging to 'The Freeman Family'.

Please join The Organ Donor Register, if you haven't already.

In the words on the t-shirt we were all given to wear in Apeldoorn, Holland, at The European Heart & Lung Transplant Championships in 2012;

Please don't take your organs to Heaven
Heaven knows we need them here on Earth.

Judith Caulkin

Foreword

I have always been in good health. So when I was asked to write a foreword for this book, I was completely unaware of the courage and enduring optimism that exists within the transplant community. I had not realised, for instance, that a poorly functioning heart can lead to having your legs amputated; I had not known that people with congenital heart defects and drastically lowered lung capacity could sometimes barely manage to get out of the bath without struggling for breath; I had not imagined that a call from the hospital with news of a potential transplant match would require such haste that barely a moment was left for packing clothes; and neither had I spent much time considering that the ability to breath without total reliance on bottles of oxygen is a gift that not everyone receives.

A nice sunny picture to reflect the sunshine within the pages of this book. Conrad and his family on holiday in Turkey last year. His wife Clare at the back in the big floppy hat, Alice on the left, then Mabel, Conrad and Violet.

The bravery of the people in these pages leaves me marvelling at their determination to live life to the full, sometimes in the face of desperate adversity. There are tales of runners and riders, footballers and table tennis players, mothers and fathers and many others. And what shines through is their simple desire for the very things that we all long for – health and happiness. These pages are full of real people, young and old, with lives that are no different to yours and mine, other than the fact that parts of their bodies don't work quite so well; they are full of tales of people who have had to battle, and hope, and pray, for things that most of us take for granted; and most of all they are full of hope and optimism. As Beth (one of the contributors to this book) says, illness does not define an individual. This book bears testament to that fact, time and time again.

But this book is not only about people who have received transplants. It is also a book illustrating the great selflessness and sacrifice on the part of the organ donors and their families. In the depths of their suffering they are willing to give, in order that others might live. It is a story that is often repeated throughout these pages, yet one that never fails to amaze me. Every time an organ is donated, a life is changed. This book is a thank you letter from all of those people that have received an organ transplant.

I am honoured to be a part of this book portraying all these courageous people.

Conrad Burdekin

This foreword for A Second Chance at Life is written by Conrad Burdekin, who is a very down to earth, young, family man with no prior connection to Organ Donation and all it entails. He is someone I regard as a good friend who shows compassion to everyone he meets and connects with adults and children alike through his love of words – he is an established writer, a brilliant poet and I felt he would give a sympathetic view of transplantation and organ donation from an outside looking in perspective.

He doesn't disappoint.

Judith Caulkin

Foreword by Professor Dark

For many of us on the staff of the Freeman Hospital, heart and lung transplantation has been the focus of our professional lives. It is thus a huge pleasure to read this book from the FHLTA, with its many fascinating stories.

Thus we have accounts of what goes on in the organization of a transplant, and what happens in the operating rooms. We have the perspective of the most senior clinicians. But most of all, we hear the stories of individual patients, recipients of hearts and lungs (and sometimes both), and from all ages.

These accounts are often happy, although many are tinged with sadness. But all of them speak of courage, starting with the huge bravery of just going ahead with the transplant, of agreeing that the surgeon's knife is the only way forward. Often when accepting a patient onto the waiting list, I will start with a comment about the bad news is that they are "bad enough for a transplant". The good news is that we can do something about it! But we never doubt the huge commitment made in saying "yes" and the courage that making such a huge step takes.

The stories epitomize many of the good things in transplantation, with return to health, and a new level of activity, of which the huge involvement in sport is an inspiring example. This involvement also illustrates the very significant role of the FHLTA. The Association is there with support for patients and families from the word go, has contributed again and again, over the years, to the clinical programme, and has made the words "Freeman Hospital" known around the world.

Finally, we must not forget that the clinical "team" at the Freeman is one of the best, and most cohesive, in the country. We pride ourselves as working in that "team", the combined results producing more that any individual efforts. All our patients, their families and the FHLTA have been and remain a key part of that "team".

John Dark
Consultant Cardiothoracic Surgeon at Freeman Hospital and
Professor of Cardiothoracic Surgery, Newcastle University

From the Chairman

As Chairman of the Freeman Heart and Lung Transplant Association it is my privilege to support recipients and their families before, during and after transplantation. Witnessing the often incredible improvement in the quality of life in so many people is awe inspiring and experiencing the friendship and support from the wider group is an honour.

I hope that this book will provide a glimpse of how lives can be saved and enriched through the gift of receiving an organ transplant. Many people continue to die waiting for a transplant often because families shy away from discussing their wishes if the unexpected was to happen.

However as this book demonstrates many people now go on to live happy and fulfilling lives because of a successful heart and/or lung transplant.

It is therefore impossible to talk about the benefits of transplantation without recognising the difficult decision that the donor's family undertook at a point where they faced the loss of their loved ones.

Therefore this book is dedicated in thanks to those that have given hope to so many.

Derek Airey
Chairman FHLTA

The Stories

My Life Story

Maggie Cowman

I was born in Wimbledon, South London and at the age of two my family moved a short distance away to Carshalton, Surrey, where I spent the next eighteen years. I was fortunate to attend a local Junior School where sport featured widely then on to Wallington Grammar School which continued to feed my passion for playing sport. I played hockey, netball, badminton, tennis and cricket for the school and local club teams. As time went on I concentrated on hockey and cricket as my main interests. I was selected for the England U25 ladies cricket squad and was fortunate enough to

spend several weeks touring India with that team in my early 20's. I went on to represent the full England team against the West Indies but my playing days were cut short when I joined the West Yorkshire Police; working shifts left little time to play so I had to content myself with playing in the local leagues as and when I could. I did this until, into my 40's, I decided to take a further step back and do some coaching for the local youngsters as a way of giving something back for the years of pleasure I had playing sport.

This is when things started to go seriously wrong for me. Whilst I was young and very fit, I never ailed for anything so it was a problem that in my forties I started to suffer with repeated chest infections. No sooner had I got rid of one that the next one followed. A few years of this and using an inhaler for late onset asthma, as my GP advised, my health was on the decline. As I neared 50, I developed severe breathing problems and had to leave the job I loved because I was deemed unfit to do it.

A new Respiratory Consultant had arrived at the local hospital and I asked for a referral to see her. I got the appointment and after tests she finally diagnosed me as suffering from Alpha I Antitrypsin Deficiency which causes COPD type symptoms. In layman's terms, my liver doesn't produce an enzyme inhibitor that is there to protect your lungs if you get an infection. Every infection damaged my lung tissue and by the time I got this diagnosis my lungs were working at less than 20% capacity so I had to use an electric buggy to get around outside the house. This was such a tremendous difference in my quality of life and had happened in less than ten years.

I was then told that this condition cannot be cured. The only chance was to try for a lung transplant. I was so desperate that I was never going to turn down any chance for a better life for myself and my family. I had tests and a four day assessment at Freeman Hospital and eventually they agreed to put me on the list for a transplant.

I was on the waiting list for 18 months and had 5 false alarms. These are when a possible donor is found but either because the donor organs are unsuitable, damaged or diseased or they find that you are not a near enough tissue match, the operation does not go ahead. A difficult time, as my health was deteriorating all the time and I was worried that the window of opportunity would pass me by. We finally got the call on 15th July 2010 and this time the transplant of two replacement lungs could take place.

After a seven hour operation I spent four days in intensive care before I came round and could breathe on my own. My husband sat watching me while I lay there with tubes coming out of various parts of my body. It must have been a nightmare for him and in truth I remember nothing of it at all. When I eventually came round I was in a High Dependency Unit for a week and then on the ward for several more. I was black and blue and it took 5 weeks before I was allowed home for the first time. While I was in hospital, my family and friends didn't visit because of the infection risk but they did a grand job of writing letters and cards which arrived daily and kept me in touch with the real world.

"Every day is a gift."

After a three month period, when contact with others was restricted, the doctors then advised that exercise and fresh air were important. They asked me at this point what I hoped to achieve now I had my new lungs and I had two things to tell them. Firstly, I wanted to represent England again at sport and second, to be the longest surviving lung transplant patient that they had!!

The summer after my operation I decided to have a go at croquet and soon became hooked. I am competitive by nature and took every opportunity to play in my first season. Then the next year I played at various tournaments to try to develop my game.

At the beginning of 2014 I was offered the chance to go to the Women's Golf Croquet World Championships in Cairo and said yes straight away. It's important to take opportunities when they arise. The average life expectancy of a lung transplant patient is ten years, although of course if I am going to be the longest surviving one I hope that I will have a bit longer!!

Cairo was the most amazing experience for me. It took me by surprise that I was so emotional about just being there and I was so proud to wear an England shirt again. I narrowly missed the cut from the group stage but went on to play in the Plate Competition which I won giving me a lovely trophy to bring home.

It's now 4 ½ years since my operation and I am already looking forward to the summer of 2015 and taking part in more croquet and transplant events.

My Journey

Andrew Drysdale

I wanted to start this piece by thanking the selfless person that enabled me to actually be writing this. Organ donation is often a taboo subject and it's understandable; nobody likes to talk about death, we will all live forever, right?

I myself feel rather fraudulent. I never had years and years of debilitating disease; I was always able to lead a very active and joyous life. I visited some great places in the world, received a good education and landed a good job. Then one day, I was told, from what seemed rather an unusual request for an ultrasound scan, that my heart was very weak and enlarged. So consider this as day one of my journey. Two days later, I was told I would need medication to stabilise my "condition". I was admitted to a cardiac ward, feeling pretty well. I was asked a couple of times if I was okay during my time there, to which I answered that I was fine. Then on the evening of day six, I was told I had a palpitation which was off the scale so I was moved to a high dependency cardiac unit in a room on my own. From there I took a drastic downhill tumble and became bedridden. It happened so quickly; the previous 2 days I had been walking, talking and having fun with visitors – now they could hardly read my blood pressure!

Day eight came and my parents were called to come to the hospital early and they simply told us they had done all they could. They knew of The Freeman Hospital which has a renowned cardiothoracic department. I was immediately transferred there and on arrival went through a number of procedures. Once my condition was relatively stable, within a few hours of being there my parents were told I would need a heart transplant. It was only eight days earlier that I had attended what we all thought was a strange ultrasound of my heart. My heart was now working at only 10% of normal capacity. I was elevated onto the European priority list for a heart; the first suitable heart would be mine. Nothing suitable came and on day ten I signed a consent form for a bi-vad, a device that basically takes over the function of your heart. Then a call came: a good, healthy match was found! It crept into the early hours of day eleven and I had received my new lease on life!!

Myself and Brianna at The Angel of The North.

I woke the next day and I have never looked back since. I relocated within a year from my home city of Leeds to London, the nation's capital. I enjoyed two years there, where I got to work on The Olympic Games. I met some amazing new friends, had a lot of fun and was able to create a professional network that enabled me to gain a transfer to Canada. I did it!! I went all out and moved countries on my own. I decided that I needed to fulfil my life, enjoy all aspects of it, learn new things, meet new people and experience different cultures. I have had the opportunity to enter and succeed in The British, European, Canadian and World Transplant Games. I relocated to Vancouver, with my now beautiful wife, having got married in 2014. She is my day to day support and keeps me on the straight and narrow. She helps to keep me healthy and inspires me to keep going in all I do. I am heavily involved with a Transplant Dragonboat Team aptly named Gift of Life, here in beautiful British Columbia, Canada.

Our wedding day, Sept 6th 2014.

The Gift of Life

Robert William Brunton

For thirty nine years I've done nothing
Because of my heart and its ills
My life was none existent
I was only alive 'cos of pills

Then on my fortieth birthday
A family I've never yet met
Donated to me a present
One which I'll never forget

And with the skills of the surgeons
And the present, donated to me
Not only did I see forty one
I can't wait for two thousand and three

I've competed in the transplant games
I've even ridden a bike
I never get a bus anymore
I put on my shoes and hike

Without a person's donation
Or the skills of a surgeon's knife
At the tender age of forty
It would have been the end of my life

So please become a donor
And give someone a life
Because without my donation
My husband would not have a wife

Written by the late Bob Brunton, (died 2003), from the perspective of his loving wife, Christine.

My Chance to Live

Carole Macfarlane

I am fifty six years old and have been married to my husband Donald for the past 37 happy years. We have no children and live in the Scottish Highlands.

After two and a half years of tests, I was diagnosed with LAM (Lymphangieleiomyomatosis) in November 1997 at the age of thirty seven. There is no treatment or cure for this disease and life expectancy is about 10 years. I tried never to say "why me"? "Why not me"? How could I wish this terrible disease on to someone else?

We tried to remain positive over the years and not let it rule our lives but my quality of life slowly declined. Eventually in May 2003 I had to give up work after twenty six years' service, which was quite a blow and a big adjustment to our lives.

I was accepted onto the transplant list in January 2005 by which time I was on oxygen 24/7 and needed a wheelchair to get about. The thought of transplant didn't daunt me and Donald at all. What other choice was there? I had no quality of life and I knew LAM would kill me sooner or later so this was just a natural progression for us. I was looking forward to it. Don't get me wrong, we were well aware of the risks involved and knew many things could go wrong, but we had to give it a go.

I underwent a double lung transplant on 1st August 2005 at the Freeman Hospital, Newcastle, when I was 46 years old. I had quite a rough time of it. I was put into an induced coma for three and a half weeks, during which time my heart had to be shocked three times and I went through a serious phase of rejection. When I eventually regained consciousness I had lost all my muscle and could do nothing for myself. I couldn't even hold a cup. I had to learn to feed myself, wash, walk, climb stairs, but every step was a triumph. I worked really hard, day by day, to regain my strength and was home within seven weeks of my transplant. The care of the nurses and doctors could not have been better and I have a great support network. It has been a slow process to regain my strength but I see improvements every day.

I tell this, warts and all, not to put people off, but to emphasise that it is so worth it. My experience was quite traumatic but I would go through it all again. There were other transplants carried out while I was in hospital and the recipients didn't have the same difficulties.

If I had to die next week I would have no regrets. Everything has been so worth it for the quality of life I have gained. It is absolutely fantastic to be able to breathe normally again, to have a life with my husband and to have my independence back and feel enthusiastic about life.

I would encourage anyone thinking of transplant to GO FOR IT. The pluses far outweigh the negatives. To give you an idea, in the

"It truly has been a gift of life. Without the generosity of my donor and their family none of this could have been possible."

space of five months post-transplant I went from being in a wheelchair to spending the night dancing at Donald's company dance. I have come on in leaps and bounds and people cannot believe the change in me. I can now do everything I could do before LAM although I am a bit older and slower!

Fast forward to 2015.

The above article was written by me, not long after my transplant, for inclusion in a book for LAM patients. Nearly ten years on I am still in good health and enjoying life. Transplantation has made such a difference to my life. In fact, I wouldn't still be around without my gift of new lungs.

It has to be said that none of this would have been possible without the support of my husband, family and friends, doctors and nursing staff, (pre and post-transplant) and most of all, my donor and her family.

"I know very little of my donor but I am so grateful to her and her family for giving me my chance to live."

NHS Organ Donor Register:
0300 123 23 23
www.organdonation.nhs.uk

Was It Worth The Fight?

Debbie Burdon

Absolutely!!! My name is Debbie and at the time of writing I am 36 years old. This story is about my journey through a double lung transplant, staring death in the face and surviving. It was the hardest fight I have ever faced, although worth every second. It has provided me with a second chance

Weekend at Chester enjoying life.

at life – I do not intend to waste it! I owe my life to my amazing donor and their family who have given me the most unbelievable gift......life itself. Thank you for your amazing kindness, I will be eternally grateful.

I was born in 1978 on a cold, very snowy 18th November. I was unwell as a child and at 6 years of age was diagnosed with Cystic Fibrosis, a life-long condition which led to a road of treatment, physiotherapy and horrendous coughing. I was fortunate to have a family who always encouraged me in everything I wanted to do – dancing, swimming, cycling and athletics. I was treated no differently to my younger brother, who luckily does not suffer from the same condition. Treatment, physio and coughing just became part of my life and who I was.

I got on with my life and was pretty healthy for someone with CF. I grew up; apparently (depending on who you speak to), attended college and found myself a good job. Things seemed great, however, I was always told by Dr Bourke and my CF Team at the Royal Victoria Infirmary in Newcastle Upon Tyne (who are absolutely fantastic) that one day I would need a lung transplant – I did not believe them......how wrong I was!

At the age of 30 I developed pneumonia and was admitted to hospital urgently. My lung function and oxygen levels dropped significantly. All I remember is wanting to die and begged for someone to take the pain away... anything to make it stop. I pulled through, although never regained my previous strength or abilities. I began to deteriorate and ended up in a wheelchair, on oxygen, lost my independence and could no longer do the things I had loved. I hated how I had become, what this illness had done to me!! I felt so angry, so useless and extremely frustrated.

I was informed by Dr Bourke that I was in the "window of opportunity" for a transplant (he had spoken about this window on a number of occasions). I was still in denial and was convinced that a transplant was not what I needed and not where I was headed. I gradually became worse and used all my energy breathing, coughing up blood and trying to function. I was drained a lot of the time and slept more than I ever had before. After a long fight in my head, speaking to family and friends, research

Difficult times, though still making the most of things.

and numerous questions answered by medical professionals, I knew deep down what was needed – a double lung transplant. I could not continue living the way I was as I knew I would die... I did not want to die! It was the hardest and most challenging decision I have ever made and it drained me physically and emotionally. I was terrified of what it meant for my future, fearful of the unknown – did I even have a future? This huge operation would either save me or kill me and the result was out of my control.

I was referred to The Freeman Hospital Transplant Team for assessment – (more amazing people). I did everything necessary to get onto the list as I needed this, even though I didn't really want it. The papers where signed, a plan was in place and my bags were packed, all I needed was "the call".

On 25 October 2012, after 4 false calls and a 16 month wait, (what I can only describe as an emotional rollercoaster), I received the call I had been waiting for. My mam, dad and brother took me to The Freeman Hospital and from then on everything happened so quickly. Every emotion, thought and feeling you could possibly imagine I experienced that night. At 5am on 26 October 2012 I was taken to theatre……..was I ever going to wake up????

I was in Intensive Care for 4 days in an induced coma so my body could recover following the trauma of the 10 hour operation. Apparently I had been given enough sedation to knock out a small elephant and I still managed to rise from the bed (stubbornness is one of my strong points….. why was anyone surprised). The first thing I remember, drifting in and out of consciousness, was hearing my dad's voice, I could hear him saying my name. When I did wake up properly I was not quite sure what had happened; drains, tubes and machines were hooked up to me. Professor Dark (the surgeon who performed my transplant) came to introduce himself — I will never be able to thank him and his team enough for everything they did that night to this day and each day forward. I was moved to The High Dependency Unit a few days later and then to Ward 38 where I began the road to recovery, not really knowing what was in store for me although I was ready for the fight. I had made it this far and I was not giving up now — told you I was stubborn. I noticed I could breathe, properly and easily — how amazing did this feel? No wheezing, no coughing, no blood…..weird, very weird, although fantastic. This is all that I had known my whole life and now it was gone!

I was discharged from hospital a few weeks later and continued to improve with a few hiccups along the way. My immune system rejected my transplanted lungs twice within the first 6 months. I always thought that rejection meant death although this was dealt with immediately and effectively, with such calmness. In essence my life had turned around in such a short space of time. A few weeks ago I was thinking, "How long have I got to live?" and now all I could think was, "What can I try next?" I learnt my new regime of medication along with the do's and don'ts of post-transplant. I regained my independence and could live my life again. Every day I thought and prayed about my donor and how this person and their family, who I knew nothing about and who I had never met before, gave me this amazing gift which I had no intention of taking for granted.

The first event I remember was Christmas and what a celebration that was. Lots of dancing and parties; I could dance which was brilliant and I just kept on dancing. People started to notice massive changes in my ability and could not believe it.

Final climb to the summit of Sergeant Man in the Lake District – such a personal achievement

One thing I had always wanted to do was to stand on the top of a mountain and that is exactly what I did. My friend has done this for years and he promised he would help me. We trained every week, twice a week. I was determined – I had to do this. We slowly increased things and took it literally step by step, starting off with hills and then bigger and bigger challenges. The first time I reached the top I cried, kissed a stone and placed it on the cairn. I had waited so long to do this and thanks to my donor, their family and a medical team of fantastic professionals it was all made possible.

In the summer of 2013 I took part in a 14 mile walk for the CF Trust, raising a little money for the charity whose research had kept me alive. Yes, 14 miles … before my transplant I could barely walk 14 steps. In addition to this my friend and I went on the most amazing adventure – a road trip from England to Italy, stopping in Amsterdam, Switzerland, Germany and eventually in Lake Garda, Italy…..”WOW!!!” is all I can say. We drove up to the breath-taking Dolomite mountains and hiked up 2 of the ranges, one being Tre Cimé. I was so overwhelmed – the view, the silence, the achievement……how proud of myself was I? I had seen nothing like it in my life, it was phenomenal.

Since then I have done so many things I love. Simple things such as walking my dog feels so great and breathing in itself (without oxygen and with ease). I have been able to go back to the gym, cycling and swimming – I feel more like the “old me” before I became so unwell. I have had numerous trips to the UK and holidays to Spain, Cyprus and let's not forget Italy. I have visited friends, formed new relationships and I am now back working full time. In a nutshell “I have my life back”. I feel I have a future that I can look forward to instead of dreading what may be.

Well, it is almost 3 years since my transplant and I decided this year to take part in The Transplant Games in Newcastle; this is something I

I did it – a truly amazing moment and the most amazing views I have ever seen at Tre Cimé in the Dolomites, Italy

never thought would be possible. I will be involved in a number of events including swimming, cycling and running. I have been training so hard since January and have met some amazing people along the way – all of us have our individual story to tell. In June I took part in a 5km women's cycling time trial event, my first ever event and to my utter shock received a bronze medal. I could not believe it... I was so chuffed. I am really looking forward to the big Transplant Games with Transplant Sport. I am a little nervous as I'm not sure how well I will do, although for me it is not about winning medals as I have the best prize anyone could ever have – life. It is about being able to take part and a personal achievement.

My journey so far has been amazing and I plan for it to continue. I feel so privileged to have such a huge amount of support from family, friends and medical professionals. They carried me when I gave up and have since watched me improve day by day, regaining my independence and my life. A song that always reminds me of my transplant is "We Are the Champions" by Queen and I become very emotional when I hear it. The words feel appropriate and always lift me up. My journey has been difficult, painful and petrifying at times, although I always kept on fighting and will continue to fight. I feel like I have won, however, the real champions are my donor and their family, the amazing CF Team at The Royal Victoria Infirmary and The Transplant Team at The Freeman Hospital, especially Professor Dark and the theatre staff who saved my life that night.

"Without any one of these people I would not be here telling you this story. They have made everything possible and my life worth living. I am so blessed, grateful and thankful everyday – all of you will always have a special place in my heart."

I'm not sure what else there is left to say. The question I asked at the beginning – "Was It Worth The Fight?" and I still say "Absolutely!"
"Did I make the right decision?" Absolutely.
"Would I make the same decision today?" In a heartbeat.

Thank you for coming along on my journey and sharing it with me.

Ready for my first cycle as part of The Freeman Heart and Lung Transplant Team – 2015, exciting times.

Our Local Hero

John Barrass

(written by Emma Barrass, John's granddaughter)

In December 1949 John Barrass was born. Alpha1 Antitrypsin disease is a rare blood disorder which is hereditary in all males in the Barrass family. The disorder can then lead to Emphysema.

My Grandfather John with his wife, my Grandmother Margaret.

John grew up a happy child and turned into a gentleman who was the life and soul of the party. His career started off as an Electrician. Later on in life he and his wife Margaret became Landlord and Landlady of the Kings Head pub in Crook, County Durham. Unfortunately John smoked and this reacted with the blood disease, leading to Emphysema. John was then told he would need a double lung transplant, to which he had to ensure his lifestyle was changed. From there on in, he and his wife moved out of the pub and John quit smoking and drinking because he knew he had to help himself.

In 1991 his eldest daughter Teresa had some news; she was expecting a child. This changed John's outlook on life, it gave him something to fight for. From then on his favourite saying was, "I'm determined I'll see my grandchild become an adult". In October 1991 John's granddaughter, (myself), Emma was born. As the Emphysema took its toll, John was

My mam Teresa with her dad, John just after his transplant.

confined to a wheelchair and oxygen 24 hours a day, but he still kept fighting.

On 23rd April 1997; John's wife received a call to say a suitable donor had been found and an ambulance would collect them in 20 minutes to take him for the life changing operation. When they arrived John was prepared for theatre whilst Margaret was shown to the family room for the next of kin to stay whilst their loved one was in for the operation. At 11pm, John was taken for the operation and he returned at 7am on 24th April 1997, onto the ward, the operation had been a success. Margaret, Teresa and Tara, John's youngest daughter, were taken to see him at around 10am.

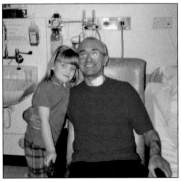

Above left: John with Tara and eldest grandson, Jack. Above right: with his youngest granddaughter, Mia. Left: Me and my granddad just after transplant.

After having the double lung transplant, John was allowed home two weeks later. It was as though he had a new lease of life. He no longer needed the oxygen and gradually became more active in his day to day life. Over the years he became a grandfather of three, he taught them all to ride their bikes, how to swim and be spoilt rotten! He also became a first aider of an under 11's football team and lived life to the full.

Unfortunately in 2009, twelve and a half years after the op he succumbed to pneumonia and organ failure. He slipped away at 59 years old.

"To anyone who has a loved one, family or friend, in need of a transplant, as hard as it is, it does get easier. If it hadn't have been for the donor I wouldn't have known my grandfather, but after the op he was so full of life, it was amazing to watch and experience. Transplantation is the gift of life and I experienced how hard he fought to survive; stay strong, there is light at the end of the tunnel."

At Jack's prom in 2014 after grandad died.

Genetic Family in Crisis

Frances Downey

My son Brian was born on 2nd March 1988, 6 weeks premature and was in The Special Care Baby Unit for 3 months of his young life fighting for survival; my wee angel had a blockage which required surgery at 1 hour old. He then got an infection and the x-ray showed that his heart was on the opposite side and he had a hole in his heart, which closed with medication. My brave little man survived by the love and dedication of doctors and nursing staff at The Royal Maternity Hospital, Belfast. Brian then developed a blockage on his right kidney and bowel problems which he overcame with the help of meds. When he was 21 months old, my whole world fell apart as my son was diagnosed with Duchenne Muscular Dystrophy and Heart Disease and was going to die. The people of Andersonstown and Belfast collected for him to be brought to Lourdes.

Brian was a beautiful, brave child, so happy and didn't complain, with the most gorgeous smile.

Everyone loved him, even the nurse who he locked in a linen cupboard with a toy mouse, nearly giving her a fright. He was a mischief maker and was forever hiding my purse. One night I thought 'relaxation needed' so I put cartoons on for him and the safety gate on the living room door. I had candles all around my bath, put perfumed oils in and soft music on then Brian changed the cd to Blue eyes by Elton John, full blast through the roof! I fell out of the bath with shock so it became his favourite song, the words of the song were Brian all over.

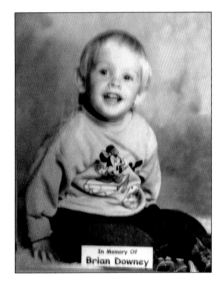

I was so proud of my son and was glad I was his mother even though it was for such a short time.

My Angel, Brian was born March 1988 and went to sleep in August 1991.

I was then told that I was a carrier of Duchenne Muscular Dystrophy and I had Cardiomyopathy.

I was already having another baby, my son Aiden, who was born in July 1992. I was told that there was a one in four chance my other child could also have it but Aiden was tested and was, thankfully, clear of DCM.

For 3 years I kept having blackouts and other turns which were quite bad until one day in Sept 1994, I collapsed. I woke up in Coronary Care Unit at Royal Victoria Hospital Belfast diagnosed with Atrial Fibrillation and Dilated Cardiomyopathy. These conditions could both be fatal and my first thought was, "Omg, who would look after my young son?" as I was a single parent. As Aiden had a speech problem, it was worrying how he could call for help if needed but he was amazing.

I got a disabled helpline installed and he learnt to be my Carer at aged 3. He could press the helpline to get me help, got me water and fixed my pillows. He made me breakfast in bed which consisted of an uncooked egg straight out of the box and put in an egg cup, dried bread , knife and butter, then dandelion weed from my garden, all with a big smile on his face!

For 20 years I just carried on with as normal a life as I could. I set up and ran a carer's support group, the first one in West Belfast, at the old Beechall and was chairperson for 9 years. I became a volunteer for CAB and Belfast Carer Centre, also Carer's Northern Ireland. I also went to Queens University where I gained a Certificate in Community Work, (distinction) based on my young sons' life story, called, "In the name of Brian" which is part one of the book I am writing, the second part is called "I believe in Angels" being written at the moment.

I became so ill I had to give the support group up so I started making crafts. I make and sell baby baskets voluntarily to help raise much needed funds for The Special Care Baby Unit. I continue to do this when I am well. 'Brian's Baskets' was set up in my son's memory; I have sold baskets in hospitals, Kennedy Centre, Bow Street Mall and other shopping centres.

I spent a lot of time in and out of hospitals with heart failure in between caring for my son and selling baskets. I just carried on until August 1994 when once a month I was hospitalised, my son had to go into respite care. It nearly killed me having to leave him.

I was told by my Cardiologist that I may need a heart transplant in the future, I deteriorated and Freeman Hospital were attending their clinic at City Hospital, Belfast, when I was given an appointment in 2012, which I attended but wasn't too ill then.

Then January 2014, I was referred to The Freeman for a 3 day assessment but tests revealed I was very ill and was kept for 10 days.

My Carer had to be sent home and I was told without a heart transplant I was running out of time. I was given 3 choices:

1. Ivad machine to keep me alive, waiting for a transplant.
2. Heart Transplant
3. Imminent death

I didn't want to leave my son Aiden, I wanted to live for him so I chose to wait for a Donor and go on the list to have a heart transplant. As I was getting worse I was placed on urgent. For a few weeks in Feb and March I wasn't going to make it due to my body shutting down. My poor son would lose me.

The day before I got a donor I went into a deep sleep, which I never do. I had my phone beside me and woke up with a jolt, to it ringing.

I had 15 minutes to wait for the ambulance to take me to Belfast International Airport for a medical plane (dinky toy) to airlift me to Freeman Hospital. I experienced fear, shock and other feelings while I waited for the longest hour ever to see if the donor heart was a match.

Then, theatre.

My brave and courageous son Aiden sat beside my bed in ICU watching me fight for life for 2 days then my beautiful, kind, caring sister arrived from Perth, Australia to help care for me. I had a tough battle to stay alive and had problems with Kidneys Dialysis, bowel stopped, body salts, blood transfusion and a reaction to drugs. My battle to survive started, I wasn't going to give up that easily, I was determined to live and fight back. I had my heart transplant on 21st March 2014, woke up long enough to wish my mum a happy birthday on 24 March, also Brian's birthday was on 2nd March; I felt that my little Angel, Brian helped me through this terrible nightmare.

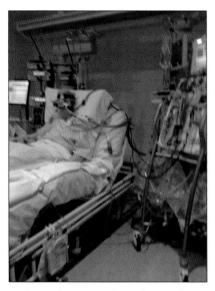

21st March 2014, taken after my heart transplant.

With my sister who flew from Perth, Australia, to care for me during and after my transplant.

"I would not have got my life back after over 20 years of illness except for the most kind, generous gift I received from my Donor and Family, The Gift of Life, which I will cherish and I will live life to the full."

I got my Miracle, I'm Alive!

Before that I couldn't even make tea or put my shoes on, walk far, climb stairs or have a normal life. Now I can walk, climb stairs and have more energy but I am on anti-rejection drugs for life. I had two bad episodes and the hospital thought my donor heart was being rejected. Due to the quick response I received from Drs, Surgeons and their intervention, I survived, and may get home to Northern Ireland in the next coming days.

I would like to thank my Donor and Family, relatives, neighbours, friends, fb friends and all the support I received from Heart Transplant Families UK, N.I T A (Northern Ireland Transplant Association) Patients at Freeman, Papworth Hospital, and Great Ormond Street and especially my brave

Sister, Theresa Burke, in Perth, Australia – I couldn't have done it without you, you were amazing. Also Surgeons, Drs, all nursing staff and other staff, through my struggle at The Institute for Transplantation, Freeman Hospital, Newcastle Upon Tyne.

My first year post transplant party with my son and family.

Selling Brian's baskets, 1 year post-transplant.

Birthday photo of myself and my son, Aiden.

A Tribute to Gerard Falsey – Someone who I will never forget

written by Judith Caulkin

I first met Gerard at The European Heart & Lung Transplant Games held in Apeldoorn, Holland in June 2012, where my husband and I went with our son, Richard. It was both Richard's and Gerard's first time competing in any transplant games.

To say that Gerard left a lasting impression on everyone he met would be an understatement. He was such a kind, warm and caring person who had the misfortune to be born with only one lung functioning; a fact which he talked about quite openly. Gerard received a single lung transplant in February 2011.

Gerard was Scottish and his Mum and Dad, who came with him to Apeldoorn, were very concerned that he wanted to participate in the strenuous sports regime, I think they would have preferred him to just go and watch the games

Gerard with Mum, Dad and silver medal, Apeldoorn June 2012.

but Gerard was determined and did so well in the cycling event that he was awarded a silver medal in his age group at the presentation evening for the biathlon – two events – cycling and running.

We next met Gerard in Scotland for the weekend Transplant Volleyball Tournament in October 2012, and even though he was clearly not breathing very well and was on a portable oxygen canister to help him, he discarded this and took part until he dropped and needed St John's Ambulance Staff to administer oxygen on the court, he was so involved in the team spirit of the game.

Gerard (right) with some of The Freeman Team, Transplant Sport Volleyball Tournament, October 2012

I just fled to the outside area in floods of tears as his Mum and Dad were clearly upset watching on from the side. They didn't want him to compete, just support The Freeman Team but Gerard being Gerard was having none of that.

The next time I saw Gerard was at Freeman Outpatient Clinic where Richard was attending an appointment for a regular check-up and Gerard and his Mum were in the waiting area. It was a shock to see Gerard in a wheelchair with his oxygen attached, looking so pale and thin. Sadly, it was not really a surprise when the transplant specialists didn't want him to go home, but instead admitted him to the hospital for treatment.

Gerard, of course, wanted to go home.

When we heard that Gerard had passed away peacefully at home, my son and husband went up to Scotland for the funeral along with dozens of other people Gerard had met through Transplant Games events.

There was a massive attendance and the service was very moving, as my husband told me; Gerard had arranged his own funeral, which is so typical of him, so that his devastated Mum and Dad wouldn't have to face all the pain of planning and preparation involved.

The congregation were told how Gerard had campaigned vigorously right up to his death for more people to join The Organ Donor Register, to help people understand the need for life prolonging transplants. He had done radio and TV interviews and had gone around schools to explain about transplants.

Nothing is ever permanent in this life and I think Gerard realised this very early on in his short but very remarkable life which is why he lived his life to the full, cramming everything he wanted to do into the short space of time he had here on earth.

He battled so hard, he is such a credit to his Mum and Dad.

I think of him often and will always miss him for his dry humour and attitude to everyone around him – as soon as you met him it felt as though you had known him for years.

Rest In Peace Gerard – I am proud to have known you.

Gerard Falsey
6th March 1982 – 18th December 2013

A passage from Gerard's Order of Service: (quoted with kind permission from Gerard's family)

"The kind expressions of sympathy and words of comfort received during the past days are a tribute to Gerard's life and are a symbol of his friendship to you all."

While I Breathe, I Hope

written by Derek Falsey, Gerard Falsey's brother

Gerard was born in March 1982; the third of four siblings. He was born prematurely which resulted in problems with his lungs from the beginning. After regular, severe infections which often led to collapsed lungs, Gerard was diagnosed with McLeod Syndrome in his right lung; a rare condition which affected the blood supply into the lung, so the right lung did not develop. The condition was further complicated by the development of brittle asthma in the left lung. The combination of problems led the doctors to advise our parents that Gerard was unlikely to survive beyond childhood.

Gerard and his siblings all sat on a big stone elephant at Calderslen Country Park, August 1985.

Being of a stubborn frame of mind, Gerard did survive childhood; though he did take medication daily and spent time in hospital throughout his childhood. Despite this, Gerard had a normal childhood, and managed to play football, cycle and everything else that you do as a kid. He left school and got himself a job, a nice flat and a few nice holidays. He had a few holidays with his big group of friends, but I think his favourite holiday was spent in California with his sister and brother-in-law. He visited Las Vegas whilst over there and fell in love with the place. I think it's fair to say that Gerard's lifelong passion was Celtic FC, where he was a season ticket holder for several years. He even managed to score a ticket to watch Celtic play in The UEFA Cup Final in Seville in 2003, one of the highlights of his life; even if the result wasn't the one he wanted.

By the time Gerard reached his mid-twenties, his health began to deteriorate. He had to give up work and move to a flat which was at ground floor level since he could no longer manage more than a couple of steps. His attentive team of doctors and respiratory nurses at Hairmyres Hospital in East Kilbride noticed that after each infection Gerard's lung function dropped and didn't fully recover once the infection had left. After a bout of pneumonia, Gerard's lung function dropped below 20% and the medical team at the hospital recommended that he was referred to The Freeman Hospital in Newcastle with a view to going onto the transplant list. He was assessed by the transplant team at The Freeman and in 2009 he was placed on the active transplant list.

It was difficult for him to take in at first. He knew that his health was poor and that a transplant might be required; but until he was accepted onto

the list I don't think he really believed that it would happen. Gerard spent 20 months on the transplant list. During this time his condition worsened on a daily basis, and he got to the point where he had to be fed through a tube and was barely able to stand on his own. In his 20 months on the transplant list, Gerard had nine disappointing false alarms, but his tenth call came in February 2011 and this time everything was suitable and the transplant was going ahead.

Gerard conquering the stairs in The Freeman, exactly two weeks after his transplant.

Gerard never learned the name of his donor, but he prayed for and thanked that person and their family every single day for giving him a chance. The rest of our family did likewise. To try to make the most of this gift, Gerard walked 4 or 5 miles a day most days to keep himself fit, he could eat again, have a beer with his friends and even catch the odd football match.

Gerard began getting involved with The FHLTA and took part in volleyball tournaments with The Freeman Team across the UK, and just like everywhere else Gerard went, he made many good friends there. In June 2012, Gerard went to The European Transplant Games which were being held in Apeldoorn. Mum and Dad were there to watch Gerard compete and he managed to win medals for running and cycling; something that was beyond the dreams of all of us.

Gerard also felt a duty to raise awareness of how big a difference everyone can make if they sign up to The Organ Donor Register so he began doing work with The Freeman Heart and Lung Transplant Association, (FHLTA) and was the Scottish Ambassador for Live Life Then Give Life (LLTGL). He visited schools, colleges and universities, he also gave after dinner talks at Rotary Club dinners to show everyone what good things can come of a tragic event.

Soon after the Apeldoorn trip, Gerard's health began to deteriorate again and he was diagnosed with chronic rejection. After trials of various treatments; including a course of radiotherapy, the hugely talented

transplant team at The Freeman were at a loss to explain why Gerard was suffering from so many infections and why they were unable to halt the rejection. Finally, we were told that the only option left was a second transplant. Gerard's health, however, was so poor that he was not fit enough to go onto the active transplant list. Despite his failing health, Gerard still pushed himself and continued to raise awareness of transplantation and organ donation. His last school visit was in September 2013 before he was taken into hospital with a severe infection, where he stayed for six weeks. Within a short time, the doctors advised us that all they could do was keep him comfortable, so he returned to his own flat in the middle of October. While Mum stayed with him in his flat 24 hours a day, Gerard was also looked after by an amazing team of McMillan Nurses during this time, who made sure that he was as comfortable as possible at all times. Despite fighting hard for every day of his 31 years on Earth, Gerard passed away peacefully in his sleep at home surrounded by his family in December 2013 and he is greatly missed.

> "For us, the donor's gift gave us almost three extra years with the best son, brother, nephew and friend any of us are likely to have and we will never receive a greater gift than that."

While Gerard passed away far, far too young, the kindness of his hero donor and the compassion of the donor's family meant that Gerard got nearly three extra years of life; 18 months of which were spent being fit and well and as close to normal as they could be. He was happy and our family had our son and brother back. Gerard never knew the name of his donor, but he prayed for them and thanked them every single day of his life; as do the rest of our family.

Always Have Hope

Holly Van Geffen

I was born with Cystic Fibrosis, a genetic life threatening disease that affects the lungs and digestive system. I had as near normal a childhood as was possible but as my teenage years began, the wrath of Cystic Fibrosis started to take hold. From the age of 18, instead of having sleepless nights from partying, I was having sleepless nights gasping for breath and coughing to the point of choking, I even suffered a collapsed lung. I was requiring oxygen and nasogastric feeding each night as well as intravenous antibiotics to keep me alive. When I was 20, I watched as my close friend was taken away from life by the monstrosity that is Cystic Fibrosis. My heart ached as I sat by her bedside in her final hours of life and it was in those precious moments I made the promise to her that I would do everything in my power to continue fighting CF for the both of us and beat it. These were when my first thoughts of pursuing transplant occurred and so I suppose the start of my journey to a second chance at life. It took 14 months of assessments and tests until I was finally told I was a suitable candidate for a double lung transplant. I was 22 with a lung function of 22% and the inability to wash, dress or even get myself around without help; I was desperate for a transplant to regain my much missed independence and quality of life.

Once on the list I was so poorly that I was made a priority and had calls just 2 months and 4 months after being listed. Unfortunately these first 2 calls were false alarms but in the 5th month it was third time lucky and I received the final call that was the go ahead!

My transplant surgery was straight forward and I was in recovery after 7 hours, however, the smooth start wasn't to last; I had a far from easy recovery with prolonged stays in ICU with, firstly, a severe life threatening lung infection along with

Waiting to go to theatre for my transplant.

septicaemia and secondly, acute kidney failure. Both were physically and mentally draining but it was a combination of incredible medical staff, my family and my 'always have hope' mantra that got me through those testing times. After 9 long weeks I was finally discharged from hospital and free to begin my second chance at life!

Me holding the team sign at opening ceremony of The British Transplant Games, Newcastle / Gateshead 2015.

I am now 6 months post-transplant and life is fantastic. The little things are the best; enjoying a bath or shower by myself, being able to dress without help and being able to scale the staircase without a piggyback! I'll never get over the wow feeling I get each morning when I awake from a full nights' sleep, undisturbed by coughing, feeling full of energy to start the day! My days no longer have a larger sleep to active ratio but rather the opposite, I enjoy regular bike rides and walks in the countryside but my favourite thing to do is watch the sun set.

Watching my first sunset post-transplant.

I have conquered a 3010ft mountain in Snowdonia and competed in a 5k cycle ride and 3km walk at The British Transplant Games, all would have been impossible without my transplant!

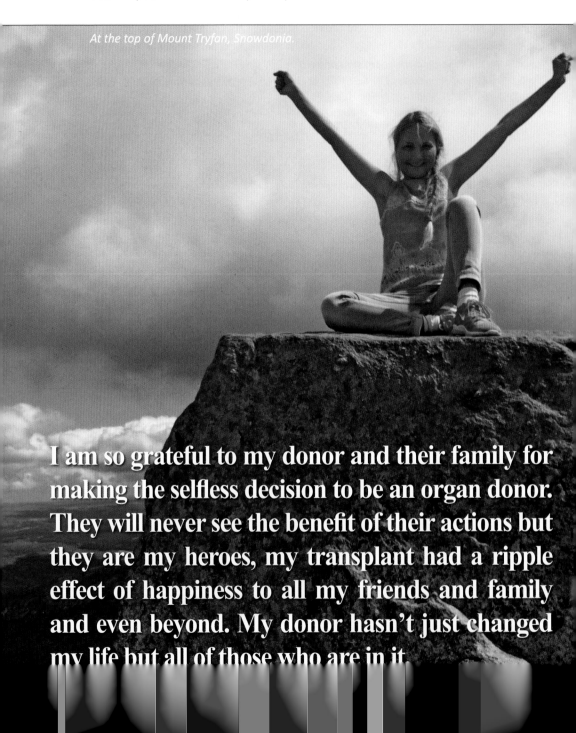

At the top of Mount Tryfan, Snowdonia.

I am so grateful to my donor and their family for making the selfless decision to be an organ donor. They will never see the benefit of their actions but they are my heroes, my transplant had a ripple effect of happiness to all my friends and family and even beyond. My donor hasn't just changed my life but all of those who are in it.

Our Story

Phillip and Joanne Watts

written by Joanne Watts

We met on my 17th birthday in February 1995. We were both fully fit and outgoing people. In 1997 I began to have a few kidney problems (along with several other medical problems too), this was due to long term type 1 diabetes (16 years to be precise).

In 2003 my kidneys finally failed and I was put on peritoneal dialysis. I struggled along on dialysis for almost 5 years while being on and off the Nottingham waiting list for a kidney transplant. I was taken off the list fairly often due to being too ill etc.

I eventually managed to convince my Nottingham doctors / surgeons to refer me to Addenbrookes Hospital in Cambridge to be assessed for a combined kidney and pancreas transplant which I had heard and read about and thought a better option for my future. I was seen in Cambridge in April 2007. Lots of tests followed, then on 4th January 2008, I got a call to say that I had been accepted onto their waiting list for a combined kidney and pancreas transplant. I was over the moon.

Just 2 days later, on 6th January 2008, I got the call to say that they had organs for me and in the early hours of 7th January I received my life saving transplant. A few problems with bleeding etc., after the initial transplant but more than happy to report that here I am over 7 years later, writing to you.

Following my transplant, in 2009 we saw and helped my Dad through cancer. He survived and we celebrated with my parents on a cruise holiday in 2010. We celebrated both mine and my Dad's good health, it was fantastic!!!

Life returned to normal, I had returned to work and Phil was working full time too. His was a very physical manual job and he worked over 50 hours most weeks and worked out at the home gym every evening, even on Christmas Day!! He took great pride in his fitness and being healthy.

> "We are not sure what the future holds for either of us but the main thing is that we are here, alive, together, and we try to make the most of our second chance at life, every day."

In mid-June 2012 I returned home one evening to find Phil in a lot of abdominal pain, I called an ambulance and Phil was seen in A&E but nothing was concluded from various tests etc.; and he was discharged with painkillers. The following few weeks saw us go to and from A&E several times, each time with the same outcome until in mid-July one doctor decided to admit him for further investigations. A CT scan was done which showed a blood clot in his heart and an angiogram confirmed that Phil's heart was failing.

We were told that eventually Phil would need a heart transplant but not for a good few years and that they could stabilise him on medication. Up to Christmas 2012 he seemed OK but then following New Year his health deteriorated quicker than anyone could have predicted.

He was eventually transferred as an in-patient from our local hospital to The Freeman Hospital in Newcastle-Upon-Tyne. This had been planned to be done with Phil as an out-patient for June 2013 but Phil was admitted to hospital seriously ill. He was transferred as an inpatient on 8th May 2013. They carried out several tests then confirmed that Phil was very sick and on 10th May he was put onto the urgent list for a heart transplant.

We were warned that he could be waiting weeks, possibly months for a suitable heart to come along. Then on 11th May, having just watched the FA Cup Final, a surgeon came onto the ward and told us that there was a heart for Phil. In the early hours of Sunday 12th May 2013, Phil was taken to theatre and also received a lifesaving organ transplant. It was not an easy run over the few weeks that followed but again, right now, I am very happy to report that he is doing brilliantly. He is almost back to full fitness and is certainly enjoying life again.

> "Our lives are continuing thanks to the kindness and selflessness of others and we thank both families each and every day for their gift."

When we were told that Phil needed an organ transplant, my initial thought was that a couple like us, just normal everyday people, cannot be lucky enough to both receive lifesaving organ transplants as we were and still are fully aware of the shortage of organs in the UK.

Life Begins At 33

Lorraine Cummings

When I was born I was described as a 'blue baby'. I had Transposition of the Great Arteries and a hole in my heart. At one week old I had my first surgery without which I had no chance of survival. I must have been a difficult baby as I didn't feed well and my breathing was laboured. Although my first surgery had enabled me to live, it did not correct the problems in my heart. Major surgery was going to be required but at one year old another hole in my heart was discovered and the operation had to be deferred until I was stronger.

Following a series of blackouts when I was three years old, I needed surgery as my lungs were not receiving enough oxygen. After that I coped quite well, despite being small and weak but my family adapted life around me. I couldn't go out in cold weather or walk very far but at that stage I was an only child so my parents were able to devote their time to me. When I started school I was 'looked after' by older pupils and at times my mum sat at the back of the classroom in case I was unwell.

When I was six years old I started to deteriorate and major surgery was the only option. The surgery was very complicated but after several setbacks I recovered and life became as normal as it was ever going to be for me. I still had restrictions in that I had no stamina, I was cold all the time and needed a lot of care at home but I was healthier than I had ever been. I was able to enjoy family life with my three brothers Jonathan, Daniel and Adam who have always looked after me as if I was the youngest instead of the eldest in the family.

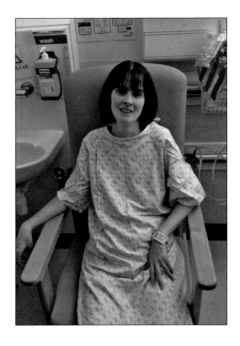

When my health declined again it was decided that I needed a pacemaker but it wasn't enough to control my irregular heart rhythm. In June 2006, I visited my mum in the library where she works and in the middle of a conversation I had a cardiac arrest and fell into my mum's arms. It must have been horrific for my mum to have to do C.P.R. on her own daughter. After 25 minutes paramedics managed to get a pulse and I was rushed into intensive care. I had an Internal Cardiac Defibrillator (ICD) implanted which would shock my heart if needed. It took a long time for me to recover and I have had memory difficulties ever since due to a lack of oxygen during the cardiac arrest.

Just when I thought things were improving I developed Endocarditis and Septicaemia and spent 7 weeks in hospital including the worst Christmas of my life. Although I was able to leave hospital I didn't really recover and I had to be airlifted to The Freeman Hospital in Newcastle in May 2010 to be assessed for suitability for a heart transplant. Despite life-long ill-health I didn't think I would ever need a transplant and was afraid that I wouldn't be suitable, however, my opinion rapidly changed when I arrived at The Freeman. Everywhere I looked mentioned transplant, every sign, every corridor, even the pictures on the walls were about transplants and this inspired a great deal of confidence in The Freeman Hospital and its team.

It was very difficult when I was told that I couldn't go home to Belfast again until I had a transplant, as I wouldn't survive the journey. My mum and brother Adam moved to Newcastle and my dad and brothers visited frequently. I had only to wait 6 weeks for my new heart although it seemed longer at the time. I made a miraculous recovery and left hospital 23 days after my transplant. I could say that is where my story ends but in reality that was the beginning. It would be impossible to adequately describe the difference in my life and the lives of my family since 07/07/2010. I have a perfect heart and circulation system for the first time in my life and am not limited in any way so I am able to enjoy and participate in family life.

"I will never forget that someone died and gave me the chance to live and I am humbled by the generosity of his family and would love them to know that my new heart is going strong and I appreciate it every day."

In the 5 years since my transplant I have been able to enjoy seeing two of my brothers getting married, I have gained two sister-in-laws — Helen and Paula and I have the most wonderful niece Sophia, none of this would have been possible without my donor, his family and The Freeman team.

One year after my transplant I competed in The Transplant Games in Belfast and won a bronze medal in badminton. That sums up the difference in my life now, I have changed from being an invalid to taking part in sports and living my life to the full.

I feel that I owe it to my donor and his family to make the most of every opportunity and I work with Northern Ireland Transplant Association to promote organ donation so that others may experience the joy of being given the gift of a life beyond compare.

NHS Organ Donor Register:
0300 123 23 23
www.organdonation.nhs.uk

The Best Medicine

Kate Parrott

It's the laughter you'll remember.
In the middle of the night,
you press the 'call nurse' buzzer
when you wake up in a fright.

Someone's always there to cheer you,
to bring a smile to quivering lips.
Someone ready with a chat, a laugh
and a cup of PG Tips.

Those lovely girls in ITU
cheer you up and wash your hair
but there's more water on the floor than you
so the Sister's in despair!

Soon you'll rattle from the tablets
listed in your little red book;
they're anti-this and anti-that;
it won't do to get mistook.

You need banter with the doctor,
as he pulls bits of your heart out through your neck,
because if you thought about it too much,
you'd be a quivering wreck.

One day you're starkers in the shower
and feel you've lost all dignity;
you just pray the fire alarm won't go
'cos then everyone will flee.

The minute you nod off to sleep
you have to get up for the loo;
the clock says that it's half past twelve;
you're out again at quarter to two!

'Dr' Hancock then arrives at dawn
with his dreaded tourniquet
to extract a trusty armful
laid out ready for display.

A porter comes to take you
off to X-Ray, ECG
just as your visitors arrive at two
and you're gone till half past three!

So, although it may be clichéd,
it's a saying old but true,
in the deepest, darkest hours,
the humour gets you through.

My Experience After Transplant

Nicole Graham

I was born in 1991 with complex congenital heart defects and was transferred to The Freeman Hospital the same day. I had my first operation a week later followed by many more in the years to follow. I suffered a stroke following an operation a week after my first birthday. My parents were always told that the operations wouldn't correct my defects but would make my heart as "best as possible."

I was never able to run, experience roller coaster rides or do lots of other physical things that my brother and sister did while we were growing up. On a family trip to Florida when I was younger, I had to watch as my family all rode the thrilling rides, thinking to myself one day I might be able to do this with them...

My heart condition deteriorated but I kept struggling on, my consultant at The Freeman couldn't believe how well I coped even though I was so poorly and my heart wasn't functioning properly.

Just before my 21st birthday in July 2012, it was decided that the time was now about right to be thinking about me going on the transplant list, a topic that had been discussed before but one which had been getting pushed to the back of my mind. I asked if I could have a big party for my birthday and a holiday before going on the list so I could enjoy a few special occasions with my family first. This was agreed and I had the most wonderful holiday and birthday party. Then a little after this I was put on the transplant list.

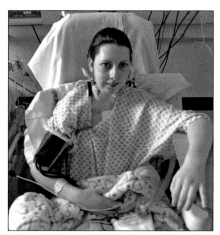

In December of that year I started to feel more tired and unwell, all over Christmas and New Year I was lethargic and didn't have the energy to go out of the house. In the January I went to see my

In Freeman ICU, approx. 3 days post-transplant, Feb 2013

consultant and he decided that I needed to go into hospital to wait for a transplant so I was admitted the following week. I was only in hospital for six weeks when the call came to say they had found me a heart. I was scared but knew this was going to change my life forever and that only after this would I be able to lead the life I had always dreamt of.

My transplant was a great success and I was only in hospital for four weeks afterwards, I have gone from strength to strength since then and have never looked back.

In September 2014 my family and I returned to Florida and this time I was right beside them in line for all the thrilling roller coasters and attractions that last time I wasn't able to go on.

Skegness Funfair, on Slingshot with my Mum (in pink trainers), Easter 2014.

They were even better than I had imagined, the thrill was amazing, and the buzz of eventually going on was overwhelming. I tried them all; Tower of Terror, Rocking Roller coaster, Dragon challenge, The Hulk, Hollywood Rip Ride Rockit, Expedition Everest to name but a few, believe me I tried them all.

Florida, Epcot Center – Sept 2014, Meeting Pluto and Finding Nemo with nephew, Jaylan and niece Tiani-Mai.

"I would never have been able to do this before my transplant and am truly and eternally grateful to my donor and their family for my gift of life and the chance to experience these amazing things."

In May of this year (2015) I went with my family to Snowdonia where we all went to Zip world where we went on "Velocity" which is "The nearest thing to flying", it is the longest zip line in Europe and the fastest in the world, it is an adrenalin fuelled attraction, the zip line is a mile long where you can reach speeds in excess of 100mph and is 500ft high! It really is an experience of a lifetime.

Next weekend I am partaking in the Colour Rush Obstacle 5K at Gosforth Park which I am really looking forward to. I exercise, swim, cycle, go to the gym with Mam regularly, all of which I was never able to do before.

In Snowdonia at Zipworld; me (on left) with my sister, Mikyla.

My Second Chance

Paul Woodward

I had my double lung transplant in September 1992. At the time of writing my story for this book it is 23 years and counting.

I was diagnosed at 7 years old with Cystic Fibrosis and I was considered very lucky that I hadn't died. Over the next few years I kept reasonably well with numerous hospital admissions. At 16 I was still playing football, I loved to play although I wasn't very good at it however by 19 my health was steadily becoming worse, but I had now managed to move into my own flat.

Over the next few years my health declined drastically and I ended up on the transplant list at The Freeman Hospital, Newcastle. After 8 months I got my call and received my transplant.

Thanks to the fantastic amazing donor family and the doctors and staff, I started to get my life back together over the next few years. I got myself fit and through this I met some amazing people and made a lot of new friends. I was socialising and getting out there doing things I had not done for years.

Me (second from left) and my mates.

I have also been very lucky to meet other transplant people who spurred me on.

In 2014 I decided to take part in both The European Heart and Lung Championships and The British Transplant Games.

The European Games were in Lithuania where I competed in the volleyball, cycling and the 100m sprint. I came home with silver in my age category in the cycling and felt very proud of myself.

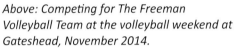

*Above: Competing for The Freeman
Volleyball Team at the volleyball weekend at
Gateshead, November 2014.
Right: Lithuania – running 100 metres*

The whole experience really got to me, watching all the transplant recipients trying their best no matter what, it really does amaze me what all these people can achieve. I have met people from all over Europe and made new friends.

Later that year I went on to compete in The British Games in Bolton which were also amazing but unfortunately no medal this time... haha.

I competed again at The British Games the following year in our home games in Newcastle / Gateshead, meeting back up with old friends and making new ones. This time I also won Gold in the 100m sprint, having rushed from the hotel to only just make the start of the race – when I arrived at the stadium the official was about to fire the starter pistol but decided to wait and allow me to run.

Gold medal for the 100m sprint.

Again, I saw wonderful people giving their all and made more friends. I hope to attend many more of these gatherings in years to come and meet even more inspirational people.

I have also been very fortunate and very proud to be asked to be a Godparent 3 times for Ellie, Lilly and Ayla and to see them grow older is brilliant.

My God daughter is the one on the left with her sister.

Being Reborn

Richard Caulkin

When I had to go home again, following my 9th false call for a double lung transplant, I knew I didn't have long left to live. After being on the transplant waiting list for 3 years, time was quickly running out. Despite being on 24 hour oxygen therapy and heavily reliant on a ventilator to help with my poor breathing, I was coughing and gasping for breath almost every waking minute. Simple day-to-day tasks like brushing my teeth or getting dressed were enough to leave me exhausted. I could barely take 5 steps without almost collapsing.

The false calls I received had always come sporadically. Sometimes months apart, at other times I went for over a year without a call. My lung function a month before my 9th call was just 5% of what it should have been for someone healthy, and was continuing to fall. Up until that 9th call, when I was told I wouldn't receive a transplant this time either, I had always believed I would have a successful transplant but now I seriously doubted I would be able to hang on long enough for another chance. And hanging on is all that I'd been doing for the previous few years. I had no life. Everything was on hold. Days consisted of a disheartening ritual of medication, physio, sleeping and forcing myself to eat to maintain weight in the hope of *THAT* call, all with my dogs by my side.

But I never gave up fighting for my life – I had been fighting from being born. I was diagnosed with Cystic Fibrosis (CF) when I was 3 years old. Despite being in and out of hospital for frequent IV's when I was younger and the intense daily routine of physio and tablets every CF patient will be familiar with, I did have a relatively normal childhood, doing all the usual things like walking the dogs, playing football with friends, making

Just back from a run with Barney, one of my dogs. Five years post-transplant.

dens in the woods, riding bikes, camping and going on family holidays. I didn't miss much school and left with 12 GCSE's, going on to do my A-levels. I graduated from Leeds University with a Masters degree in 2003. My problems started when I contracted atypical tuberculosis, an opportunistic drug-resistant chest infection, while I was working toward my PhD. I had to put my studying on hold for a year during 2005 while I underwent intensive treatment. Although the infection was cleared eventually, my lungs were left 'in tatters' and I was told a double lung transplant was my only option left.

I felt like the ground had swallowed me up when Dr Daniel Peckham, my CF specialist at Leeds, told me this as I didn't feel all that ill at the time, despite my lung function being around just 40%. However, I can never thank him enough for his attentiveness and timing on this, as when I went for my initial assessment to The

PhD graduation photo, Sept 2008. My Oxygen canister is just out of shot!

Freeman in October 2006 they said I was ill enough to be placed on the active list, but in my mind I didn't feel quite ready. As such I was listed provisionally. By December my health had deteriorated so much, so quickly that I felt the time was now right; I was on all the available treatments, but none of them were working. I was becoming so breathless I wasn't able to function on a daily basis, even with 24hr oxygen. I was re-assessed and placed on the active list with immediate effect.

In March 2007 I received my first call and remember the very mixed feelings of apprehension and hopefulness when Neil Wrightson, my transplant coordinator at the time said to me: "...don't build your hopes up but there's a possible donor". I felt a mixture of dread but also optimism for a 2nd chance; looking forward to everything I had yet to experience. I also remember thinking, with sadness, about the person whose lungs I could be receiving. What had happened for them to lose their life? Were they male or female? Young or old? I remember thinking about their family giving permission to donate their loved one's organs at such a tragic time, to help someone they didn't know and in all probability never would. The ultimate example of altruism. What extraordinary people they must be to think of others at such a time, as are all donor families.

It was at this point that the reality of my situation hit me for the first time. Up until then, it had all been hospital appointments, tests and meetings. Something I'd always been used to thanks to CF. Now I was facing the very real prospect of a major, potentially life-saving operation. Following the long overnight wait in hospital for a decision, I received news the following morning that the transplant wasn't going ahead for me. Instead, both lungs and heart were to be transplanted into someone needing both – I'd been called up as reserve in case the heart wasn't in suitable condition. My overwhelming feeling at that point was relief. Relief that I got to walk out of the hospital that morning and get on with my life the best I could. How different to how I felt following the same news that I wasn't getting a transplant following my 9th call.

At the time of my 9th call, I had been on the waiting list for 3 years almost to the day. I remember Lynne Holt, my co-ordinator, got really upset, saying she hoped she wasn't on duty for my next call as she regarded herself as unlucky for me – she had called me for all but 2 of my 9 'dry-runs'. By this point, I had all but accepted that I had run out of time. I was prepared to accept the inevitable. Every single minute was a struggle just to breathe, combined with increasingly frequent episodes of coughing up blood. No matter what my oxygen was turned up to, my O_2 saturations refused to increase beyond mid-80%. Every part of my body was tired and aching. My body was beginning to shut down.

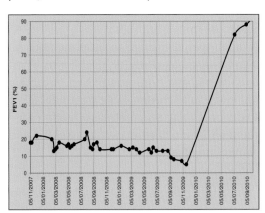

My lung function (FEV1) spanning 2 years pre-transplant to six months post-transplant.

I received my transplant in the nick of time on 21st December 2009. It was my 10th call and it came just 6 hours after returning home following that failed 9th call. At midnight, the house phone rang. Everything from this point on is a little hazy but I remember Lynne on the phone asking me to go back to Newcastle. So much for her theory that she was unlucky for me!

At The Freeman, I was so weak I remember struggling to stand whilst having a shower before being taken to theatre; I was so out of breath. I remember Lynne saying to me just before I was anaesthetised: "When you wake, you'll be able to breathe". And she was right.

"Thanks to my donor and their family for giving me a second chance. Like all donors, in the face of tragedy, your selfless decision ensures many other families get to stay together. Without them, I would not be here. Without transplantation, there is no story."

Above: At the finish line of the Bristol to Freeman bike ride, July 2015, with two of my Transplant doctors, Dr. Meachery (and his son) and Prof. Corris.
Right: Some of my medals from various sporting events, including British and European Transplant Games.

I woke up in intensive care, initially unsure of what had happened or how well things had gone. I had wires, tubes and drains in every place imaginable. Recovery was a slow and at times excruciatingly painful process, although I recovered really well. In fact I was told my whole recovery was text-book. Within 2 days of leaving ICU I was using a static bike and within 2 weeks of my transplant I was home. The surgeons, doctors and support staff at The Freeman are second to none. The number of inspiring, uplifting and almost unbelievable stories I have read in this book during the editing process is testament to that.

In the days after transplant, while on the high dependency unit, my Mam rang my Nanna and even though I wasn't really up to talking on the phone I had a few words with her. Her last words to me were: "That is all I have been waiting for." She had prayed for years for me to not have to suffer and to get a transplant to give me a future. On 26th December my Nanna died. She wasn't ill to anybody's knowledge and she died on my Dad's (her son's) birthday.

I'm continually looking for new physical challenges to push myself and to raise awareness of organ donation in the process, demonstrating what it can allow someone to achieve. I have attended numerous Transplant-based sports events, even meeting my future wife at the games in 2013. In the first half of 2015 I have taken part in a 65 mile cycling sportive, a duathlon where I finished 27th out of 134, a 24hr duathlon as a team of 5, which we won and in July 2015 I cycled 342 miles over four days from Bristol to The Freeman Hospital, Newcastle with 40+ other cyclists, including Freeman heart transplantee Kevin Mashford aiming to raise £50k for The Transplant Association, a new charity co-founded by Kevin to train nurses to recognise and treat the psychological impact of organ transplantation.

A Sudden Change of Heart

Wendy Lingham

I was 23 and life was good. It was not long before I was due to give birth. I woke to feel breathless in the night and gasping for air. I opened the window to feel the relief of being able to breathe again. I went to the Doctors about this and saw a Nurse. I was told it was normal to feel like this in the later stages of pregnancy and to invest in a fan.

The time was getting closer. As I visited a sick relative in another town who had sadly passed away, I found myself in hospital again, struggling to breathe. I still had one month to go before I was to give birth. The Nurses and Doctors had done all of their vital checks and could see nothing wrong. My baby was on the way. I gave birth by emergency caesarean to a healthy son. The following few days is where my story begins...

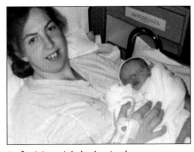

Left: Me with baby Joshua.

You're supposed to be happy after giving birth, you imagine bringing baby home, resting a few days and then carrying on with life as normal. Life was not destined that way for me. I carried on struggling to breathe and if I laid down flat I would make this horrible breathing noise. I could barely walk a few metres without feeling like I had run a marathon. The Doctors thought I had a blood clot and so I was sent off to be checked. The results came back clear. By day 5 after giving birth I was sent for a heart scan. Later that day, I was surrounded by Doctors and Nurses telling me I was in heart failure.

Heart failure? I was shocked. I had no family history of heart problems. "I think you have made a mistake" I told them. "No" they said. Then another Doctor spoke and said I had Dilated Cardiomyopathy. The strain of the pregnancy had caused the heart to enlarge which meant it was not pumping properly and this had caused the heart failure. I felt numb, my mind was all confused. I thought I was going to die. The Doctors were uncertain about the future but knew they had to take action immediately. My son was taken from me and I was sent to a cardiology ward where I was put on heart failure medication and an IV drip of medication as my body had accumulated a lot of water, which was not helping my breathlessness.

This was not the life I expected, at age 23 and only just given birth. A normal life seemed to feel like a million miles away. I returned home with my son at week 3. I never gave my baby his first bath and struggled to do the 'normal things'. Gradually, the medication made me feel a little better. I spent the next few years feeling tired on some days but coping and I was living a relatively normal life. Life again was good and I felt blessed to be alive and I even booked to go away on holiday. Life again had other plans; and I never did get to go on holiday.

By the time my son had reached his 4th birthday I was feeling breathless again. I knew that feeling as I had experienced it before. I was sent for an emergency scan and there the Doctors discovered I had a blood clot on the heart. I was admitted to hospital and received the treatment I needed to get better. I recovered well. I picked myself back up and carried on being a Mum. Six months later, I was suffering from breathlessness again. I could not believe that something could happen again so soon after and I thought I was just unfit so I began to do additional daily exercise. This did not help matters and I found myself at the Doctors complaining of breathlessness once more. I was reassured that everything was fine but if it helped I could visit the hospital. I needed to have peace of mind and so I went to the local hospital. The Doctors discovered I had a fast heart beat and it needed correcting. I had to have an electric shock to put the heart rhythm back to normal. Again, the Doctors helped me. The next few years, I found the local A&E every 2-3 months, my second home. I had a problem with my rhythm and every time I would have an electric shock to correct it. I also had community Heart Failure Nurses come and keep an eye on me, who were a huge support.

On one occasion, I was sent to another hospital to have an ablation, an operation to correct my rhythm problem. Finally, I could see some light. I was put to sleep but when I awoke, I had lost my memory, confused as to where I was and discovered I had been on a life support machine fighting for my life. My heart was just too weak to manage the operation. It was not long before my son's 8th birthday. I have no recollection of this.

My heart failure symptoms got worse. I began to get swollen ankles, slept sitting upright with a mound of pillows, constantly exhausted and vomiting, to name only a few symptoms. I was deteriorating. I knew it.

I was referred at short notice to the Newcastle Freeman Hospital. There, the Doctors listed me for an emergency transplant and I was told I was not allowed home and given only weeks left to live. By this point I was talking to people and falling asleep. I was pushed around in a wheelchair and was bedbound. I struggled to get dressed yet I kept my mind as active as I possibly could by studying Law. Three weeks later, it was time to walk up to the operating theatre and that's when it really hit me. For those last few seconds I felt really scared. I had tears rolling down my face and I had to say goodbye to my mum, my sister and my friend. I had to say goodbye to my son and tell him that, no matter what, I would always be with him.

I really wanted him to hold on to my words as I bent down and looked into his weary, big blue eyes and hugged him as tight as I possibly could. I had to think that, whatever happens, it's going to be all right. If things didn't go well I knew Josh would be taken care of. My sister, although it would be hard on her, would have cared for him, along with my friend and my mum.

If things go well I will have a healthy heart. I will be well enough to live a new life. It was a frightening situation to be in. But I had a fighting spirit in me.

Everything went into slow motion. It felt as if everything was going on around me, but everything slowed right down. And that was it. The next thing I remember was waking up in intensive care and I couldn't speak. I could hardly move my hands because I was so weak. I had lost my hearing. I was confused and I felt really rough. Really, really ill. The doctors weren't sure I would make it. I spent six weeks in intensive care, where they put me into a coma. I can only remember one of those weeks. When I came to, I had a tube in my windpipe to help me breathe. I had pneumonia and I was constantly coughing. I was scared and confused. I tried to communicate with a voice box but I was very weak and sore and I just didn't make sense. I'd lost my hearing. My kidneys had failed and I was on dialysis. My days consisted of being hoisted in and out of bed and some physiotherapy.

> "Someone – a stranger – decided that I should live."

After six weeks I was moved to a high dependency ward.

A week later my hearing started to return and I was able to speak very quietly. I managed to get out of bed to the chair and used a Zimmer frame for support. I had lost the use of the muscles in my legs. I was still on dialysis and I was exhausted. It had all taken a toll on me, both mentally and physically. I thought it was never going to end.

But I gradually began to see some improvements. With help, I managed to walk to the shower, then around the ward, pushing a wheelchair for support. I waddled like a young child learning how to walk. But it was a step in the right direction. About two and half months after the operation, my kidneys started to improve. When I could climb two flights of stairs I was finally allowed home.

I started cardiac physiotherapy. I began to see real improvements and I felt good. I went from strength to strength.

A year after the operation, I was fundraising in my town with friends, singing. (No, I can't sing!). A little while after I was biking 20 miles for the British Heart Foundation. I thought back to that day when I had been assessed for a heart transplant. I had managed two minutes on a bike, and I thought that was good. Doing the bike ride was a massive achievement. I had lived with an illness that turned me into an invalid. Riding a bike gave me a sense of freedom that is almost indescribable – and I felt proud.

*Left: Biking in the time-trial at the Transplant Sport Cycling event, 2015
Right: Myself with my son, Josh – bronze and silver medals in cycling at the Transplant games, 2014.*

When I woke up from my heart transplant I never imagined that I would be able to bike 40 miles in a cycle challenge in the Heart of York bike ride for The British Heart Foundation but I did – although very challenging, it was amazing. Neither did I ever imagine that I would have the ability to take part in all other sporting challenges that I have. I have exceeded my own expectations. Because I was so ill for years prior to the transplant and had such a difficult time afterwards, everything I continue to do is a massive achievement, no matter how small.

In 2013, I competed in The British Transplant Games for the first time. I competed in swimming, cycling and walking events. I even achieved a silver medal for cycling. I felt humbled to be amongst so many people who had faced such adversity in their life and had come through it fighting. I have attended every British Transplant Games since, as well as other Transplant Sports events, all to promote organ donation and show how it can transform lives.

My son for the first time in his life can see me well and now we can enjoy life.

I can never forget that my whole life was changed because someone signed the organ register. Someone who will never be forgotten transformed my life.

Left: Me and my medals from the TS Cycling Tournament, Silver & Bronze + Donor ride medal.

Right: Walking in the Lake District.

A Match Made In Heaven

Wendy Lingham & Richard Caulkin

King Edward's Bay, Tynemouth

We got engaged in June 2015, a day before Wendy's birthday. This new chapter of our life began on Tynemouth beach, 8 miles from The Freeman Hospital. This place holds special significance for the both us; it is the first place we both visited, completely separately, when we were allowed out of the hospital for the first time following our respective transplants. Richard in 2010 and just over a year later for Wendy in 2011.

We believe that our meeting, at the 2013 British Transplant Games in Sheffield, was down to fate and destiny. Every action you're going to undertake in your future is based on the millions of actions taken previously, and that everything does happen for a reason, as opposed to just coincidence.

At The Freeman following the Bristol-to-Newcastle ride, July 2015.

There are three elements that conjointly affect the course of one's life – fate, effort and time. Take the example of a gardener, whose plants depends on three factors: planting, rain and time. Planting represents effort and rain represents fate. If the gardener plants but there's no rain, there'll be no flowers. And if it rains but they haven't planted, there'll also be no flowers. Both fate and effort are required, as is time. This analogy relates to relationships too – you only get out what you put into it. If we act properly and perform dedicated activities, we are awarded good fortune. If we act wrongfully, we have to suffer. Over time, good fate manifests as situations favorable to our efforts and bad fate as negative situations. Destiny may even give us enjoyment or suffering without much endeavor, such as being born into a rich family, being very intelligent, having a diseased body or being born into a poor family.

As for whether two people are destined to be with each other – if there was ever a love story to make us believe in fate and destiny, it's our story. There were so many unusual things that happened to both of us outside of our control that it seems like the universe was just bringing us closer and closer together. Now we are getting married!

Celebrating Wendy's birthday.

We have thought long and hard about the situation we find ourselves in. The Lord works in mysterious ways and our previous situations, despite being traumatic, needed to happen so that we both could meet. If it is your destiny to be together then nothing will stop it. Fate says that whatever will happen will happen.

"Love what matters and hold tight to it."

If certain things in our lives had never happened, we would not be where we are today.

There is a saying, "right place, at the right time," and we definitely feel that has to do with fate. Sometimes you need to be in relationships that are not right in order to make you ready for the one that you are meant to be in. Dealing with love, however, is something more than just dealing with fate and destiny.

Love is not a thought, it's a feeling. You can't change your mind about someone once they have entered your heart. If you think that you were

In Filey (left) and Amsterdam (right).

Richard, Wendy and Joshua at the Freeman 30th Anniversary celebration dinner, May 2015.

once in love, but fell out of it, then it wasn't love you were in. When you meet "The One", you get this deep feeling inside you that never wanes – it just grows stronger with time.

Even though there may be bumps in the road, it's those bumps that make us realise just how important and fragile love truly is. We both believe that no matter how long it may take, or how complicated it may get at times, true love will ALWAYS find a way.

We are getting married. We love each other for who each of us are. We understand each other and make each other happy. If we had met earlier, or under different circumstances than we did, maybe our forthcoming marriage would not be happening. That's the thing with fate, timing is everything.

Josh, Wendy's son is 13 and completes 'our new family'. He keeps us young and on our toes, as entertaining him, for instance taking him to Go Ape for his birthday, the three of us swinging through the trees in Dalby Forest, is a new adventure for all of us together and we are looking forward to many more adventures in the future. Togetherness and happiness is what our lives are about.

Who'd have imagined that the power of organ donation would've made this possible? A match only made possible due to our donors.

Not only does transplantation work and make a difference but it can change the lives of many others. We, as a family are living proof of that.

My Hero

written by Judith Caulkin (Richard's mum)

My son is my hero
I am so proud and humbled
He has had to battle
All his life, never grumbled
To breathe
Just to breathe

His humour has kept me going
Over the years
He never gave up, always towing
He made me laugh through my tears
Even though
Every day was a struggle for him
To breathe
Just trying to breathe

He nearly didn't make it
His double lung transplant
Came just in time
To save his life
Three years waiting for a chance
To live a life
To breathe
Just to be able to breathe

His donor family contacted
They replied by letter
The fact their loved one
Had not died in vain
Lessens their pain
Happy he can now breathe
Knowing their loved one lives on in him
Letting him breathe
Finally to be able to breathe

A second chance at life
My hero
Has now become, for me
My two heroes.

Double Lung Transplant Story

Jane Holmes

I have 4 children; a son 24, a son 20 and twins aged 7. The twins were the start of my problem as when I became pregnant with them, the stress on my body brought out a condition called pulmonary hypertension. I became so ill really quickly and couldn't breathe properly, going upstairs became a nightmare. I generally turned into an old lady within weeks, from being a healthy social butterfly to using a wheelchair, a bed in the front room downstairs and a commode. I'm not sure how we got through, it's hard to put into words just how stressful, depressing and sad this time was. I felt like I spent most of my time meeting different consultants for this condition and for another, not to mention carrying twins! I also have mixed connective tissue (cousin of lupus).

My relationship with the twins' dad started to break down, (we split up altogether eventually). Thank God for my Mum! She gave up her full time caring job to look after myself and the twins when they were born. All through my pregnancy I was in and out of hospital and having to learn to inject myself with Fragmin into my stomach, which is a blood thinner.

Over the next 5 years my condition fluctuated then I was sent for the 4 day trial at The Freeman to see if I was at the stage to be put on the transplant list, another emotional time. Alas, yes I was ready. I can't remember how long I was on the list before I got a call, maybe 18 months-ish? It was a Sunday, early evening, a very long night! The donor lungs weren't very good even after being on the 'rig' and I came home heavy-hearted and I'd let too many people know I was going so had a lot of texts and phone calls wanting to know how I was doing. Then a week later, Thursday 14th March 2013, I had a 2nd call, it was the one! I omitted to tell you we had 2 house moves in this time and my eldest son, Tom and his girlfriend Becky, were having a baby and she went into labour just before my call. I was on the phone to Tom as I arrived at The Freeman, it was my first grandchild, a little girl. I then broke the news where I was after I knew they were all fine (didn't meet her for 3 months and that was at The Freeman!)

When I was admitted, I was greeted by Katie, my transplant coordinator at that time. She was lovely and I have kept in touch with her to this day, (she moved from Freeman on to Papworth). I was all over the place, happy to have the life changing op to enable me to be a proper Mum, Grandma and daughter, but if it was a no go, happy to go and meet my granddaughter. I went down to theatre laughing and waving, probably slightly hysterical.

Next thing I knew it was 3 weeks later! I'd had multi organ failure, had been on the ECMO machine, kidney dialysis and had a blood clot in my leg which burst. I could only move my eyes, it was a long road to recovery but I was alive!

There is a lot to my story and I'm glad to be here to tell it. I've been in touch with my donor's family by card, she sounds like she was a beautiful lady with a wonderful family. The best thing for me is I've been given a second chance and a new outlook on life!

P.S. I was 39 when I had my transplant and because I became 40 while unconscious, I had a massive 41st party raising £1,000 for FHLTA, also my friend ran the London marathon raising another £1,200.

"Live for the day, cup half full .... and I love my family. Without them I am nothing and that's what kept me going!"

Sam's Story

Sam Griffiths

I was born at The North Staffordshire Hospital and to begin with all appeared to be fine. However, at 6 hours old the Doctor noticed I was slightly blue. I was immediately hooked up to a ventilator and was taken to Birmingham Children's Hospital where they confirmed I had a rare and complex congenital heart defect. At one day old I had a cardiac catheter procedure and at two days old I had my first open heart surgery.

The next 8 months were spent in and out of hospital due to problems with heart function, related illnesses and most dominantly my inability to thrive. At around 8/9 months old I had my second open heart surgery. I came through the operation but had a cardiac arrest that night.

I then continued to be in and out of hospital and not long after my 2nd birthday I was rushed in due to heart failure. I deteriorated further and on Christmas Day I was sent down to intensive care and my family were told to say goodbye. The next day I was still fighting. A week later, on New Year's Day, the same thing happened and I was back on the ward with my family being told I would need a new heart as soon as possible. At this point I was put on a new experimental drug.

I was taken down to Gt. Ormond Street Hospital in London and was put on the waiting list. I went back home after a month and began to thrive and improve so my family made the decision to take me off the waiting list as we had heard nothing of a new heart at that stage, however, I continued to have various problems over the next few years, some serious and some not so serious, with another open heart surgery being performed but failing. During this time I also underwent many minor operations.

In March 2008 we went to Birmingham Children's Hospital for a routine appointment to be told I would have to stay as the scan of my heart showed the heart function had gotten a lot worse. My family knew this would mean a transplant, but Birmingham Children's Hospital wanted to try and fix a leaking valve a second time as it was this that was causing major problems. I had a metallic valve implanted and for the first 24 hours it seemed successful, unfortunately the operation put me into complete heart block, the electrical signals of the heart were all misfiring so 3 weeks later I had to have a pacemaker fitted. The valve leak had not improved.

I never properly recovered from the last hospital stint and subsequently was re-admitted to Birmingham Children's Hospital and I went through transplant assessment, this time at The Freeman Hospital in Newcastle-upon-Tyne. Having spent 2 more months in Birmingham, deteriorating rapidly, at midnight on the 7th of July we got the call we'd been waiting for and I was rushed to Freeman's Hospital where I underwent a heart transplant. The transplant was a success and I'm thankful to my donor family every single day!!!

Three weeks after transplant I returned home and the first thing I wanted to do was to learn to swim! I couldn't be in the water for more than 5 minutes before without needing oxygen!! I could finally float around in the water for as long as I wanted and stay nice and pink!!!!!

With all the incredible medical support and the love and support of my family, especially my lovely Mum, Dad, sisters and brother, I am now enjoying my life and especially my swimming! I train at least 3 times a week with my experienced Swim coach (my Dad!).

I have competed in The British Transplant Games in swimming for 5 years for my wonderful FREEMAN CHILDREN'S TEAM and have won lots of medals!! Most recently this year I competed in Bolton (2014) and won 5 Gold medals as well as winning the 'Best child trophy' in the 12-14 age

"I was given the gift of life and I'm making every second count!!"

'Best child trophy' in the 12-14 age group.

group. I not only can be like a normal child now but through my hard work and determination I am achieving things that never seemed possible! This includes all my school work I've caught up on at Madeley High School in Cheshire where I am now working at the same level as my peers!

Because of my achievements in Bolton and the hard work I've put in, in swimming, I have had the honour of being selected in representing my country at the World Transplant Games in Argentina in 2015.

This is the second time I have been selected to represent Great Britain in the World Transplant Games and I am extremely proud!! I went to South Africa in 2013 and won 4 Gold medals, 1 Silver medal and smashed 2 world records!!!

I think my story proves that no matter what odds may be stacked against you and however many times you want to give up you have to be brave and try!! Anything is possible!!!

With my Mum at the British Transplant Games, Bolton 2014.

"I am a very, very lucky lad!!!!!!"

Rebecca ... A Tribute

by Judith Caulkin and Sue Marley

I met Sue, a friend from school who I hadn't seen for years, in the waiting room at The Adult CF Outpatients Clinic, Seacroft, Leeds; it would have been around 1998.

Sue's daughter, Rebecca, I then found out, was born with Cystic Fibrosis, the same as my son, Richard; born the same year; Rebecca was born in November 1981 and Richard was born in February 1981.

How coincidental.

We kept in touch from that day on and I got to know Rebecca a little bit. Sue and Rebecca were like sisters, they were so close. They were both alike, being so bubbly, laughing at the same things and generally loving their life together as a family, despite the overhanging shadow of CF. Sometimes CF splits families up with the stress of it all and the debilitating disease makes it overwhelmingly hard for some to cope with everything it throws at them. With Sue, her husband Paul and Rebecca, CF had the same effect as with my family, it brought them even closer; the protective instinct becoming stronger and stronger.

Rebecca... doing what she loved to do, on holiday in Cuba having a drink and just enjoying her life.

At the age of 20 Rebecca was found to have contracted the bug B. Cepacia and over the next seven years became increasingly ill. She fought right to the end but as there are no drugs to treat this bug, Rebecca could not even be considered for a double lung transplant, which she was told when she was assessed at The Freeman Hospital.

Transplanted lungs can get re-infected when any of the germs are still present in the chest cavity when the damaged lungs are removed.

In the case of my son, the coordinator explained that the microbiologist had to develop a cocktail of drugs to swill out the chest cavity before the donor lungs were to be transplanted, so that not one single germ remains there; this is called bleaching.

As there are no drugs developed yet to eradicate B. Cepacia, if a transplant had been done for Rebecca, her lungs would have become re-infected and she would not have survived.

Patients are only put on the list for a transplant if they can meet a list of specific criteria, including that there is a good chance of survival post-transplant.

In Richard's case, we were told his survival rate was expected to be 50% chance of recovery and leading a life, post-transplant. He agreed to take the chance he was given and signed the forms.

Rebecca would not have had a hope of surviving the operation. CF became a death sentence for her.

Her memory lives on through her mum as she plans and prepares from one year to the next to hold fundraising events in the name of 'Becci's Fund' every year, raising money for The Cystic Fibrosis Trust to try to find a complete cure for CF and also vital research into drugs to eradicate bugs such as B. Cepacia, to give patients in the future a better chance of surviving CF, to live as near a normal life as possible.

Relentless fundraising is done by people in the hope that others won't have to face the excruciating pain and heartache of losing a child to CF.

Rebecca died 10th June 2009 at the age of 27 at home with her family around her. She packed such a lot into the short time she had, socialising, going on holidays, just enjoying her life. She worked full time up to eight months before she died and raised funds for CF whenever she could, running the Great North Run every year while she was well enough to.

Above: On completion of the Great North Run. Left to right: Husband Richard, Rebecca, Dad Paul and Mum Sue.

Rebecca had a boyfriend in her last years and because she wasn't going to let CF have the last word, she got married in hospital five days before she died because she knew she wouldn't make her wedding day on 4th September.

Rebecca was a wonderful daughter and leaves a massive hole in so many lives, especially her mum's, her best friend.

My Unknown Journey

Ryan Michael O'Connor

A couple of days before my heart transplant.

Well, I was born with a congenital heart condition that took a lot out of me, growing up. When I was 16, I went for assessment at The Freeman Hospital to see if I would be suitable for a transplant and fortunately I was.

I had my heart transplant on 23rd November 2012 after waiting for 2 years, including 9 weeks in the hospital as an inpatient because I was too sick to be at home and I also needed medicine administering to keep me going until my heart transplant.

Unfortunately, 3 days later I went into cardiac arrest and it cost me both my legs; I was amputated above the knee on both legs. The blood flow goes to the main organs before the limbs but by the time they revived my new heart, the calf muscles were dead and had to be amputated or the poison would have spread through my body and would have killed me.

After 6 months in hospital, I finally got out in February 2013 and since then I have worked my way up and am still working to get the best prosthetic legs I can get and everything is going good.

I am now doing courses in filming and doing a bit of work experience in it.

Opposite Page:
Top left and top right: The light that pushed my life. Pre-transplant I was chosen to carry the Olympic Flame. I was quite ill on the day and travelled most of the route in a wheelchair but was determined to walk the last few yards – and I did!
Centre left: At Amputee Games (me on left).
Centre: Taking part in wheelchair sport.
Bottom left: With Mum and Dad.
Bottom right: With Nana Mary.

NHS Organ Donor Register:
0300 123 23 23
www.organdonation.nhs.uk

A Star Was Born

written by Tricia Harkin (Ryan's Auntie)

For my family it was a wonderful day
It was the 24th of May
For I was born in Co. Derry
And everyone was happy and merry
Mammy got home that Friday
But as for me I had to stay
The doctors frowned so I could tell
Me the wee cretter, I wasn't well
I had a pain in my tiny heart
But wouldn't you know, that was only the start
So a name for me they had to find
But you know me I didn't mind
Time was important for all it was tough
So Ryan Michael I got, I was happy enough
When I heard of my godmother it was a little scary
But a true guardian angel- yes Nana Mary
Bye-bye to Derry and hello The Royal
Where the nurses are so kind and loyal
They sometimes get angry when I won't eat my food
But I'm too wee to tell them it isn't that good
If you ever wonder why I keep smiling
It's all because of my Great Granny Eileen
For her prayers work wonders you'll all agree
Now Eileen they'd better be all for me
I think a lot about the day
That I get home.... and I hope to stay!

♡♡♡JUNE 1994 ♡♡♡

Cretter is a local word meaning wee critter/creature/child
I wrote 'A star is born' poem when my nephew, Ryan was born in 1994.

No Place Like Home

written by Tricia Harkin (Ryan's Auntie)

Ryan from Dungiven became a hero overnight

When he received a heart transplant but not without a fight

He spent 9 weeks in Newcastle then came a donor heart

A new beginning is all he wanted but this was just the start

The surgeons battled through the night to stop his heart from failing

Complications they began to show, it wasn't all plain sailing

Circulation problems they arose but Ryan was so brave

But a lot of damage had been done and his wee legs they could not save

Back home the whole community came together with a plan

They formed a little committee to help this special man

Functions they were organised by all within the town

From both sides of the community they wouldn't let Ryan down

A poker night in Wanes World and black and white night in the club

An open mic night and donations from each and every pub

Local sports stars auctioned jerseys and many came from near and far

To take part in the "walk for Ryan" to support our special star

And when Ryan fully recovers, no matter where he may roam

There's no doubt that he will agree that there is NO PLACE LIKE HOME!!

♡♡♡2012♡♡♡

Wanes World is an indoor play centre in Dungiven.
Wane is a local word for child.
I wrote 'No place like home' when Ryan received his heart transplant in 2012.

A Second Chance of Life

Jon Comb

I suffered from Hypermobility Syndrome all my life but in 2009 I suddenly developed Cardiomyopathy. At the time I thought I had a case of the Swine Flu (this was during the big Swine Flu scare). After my initial symptoms had settled I still could not get rid of a persistent cough so went to the doctors who sounded my chest and sent me for an urgent x-ray and echocardiogram.

I was prescribed medication to control the symptoms and cardiac rehab. After a few months I was transferred to the care of The Cardiac Team at The Freeman Hospital.

All was well until late 2012 when I got what I thought was a chest infection that just refused to go away. I struggled on until my next appointment in April 2013 when to my huge shock I was told I needed to go for an assessment for a transplant.

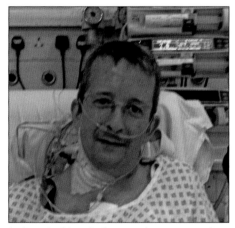

I went into The Freeman for my assessment on 23rd July and on 2nd August I was told that I would not be allowed home and that I would be put on the urgent list for transplant. My family came from all corners of the country (and France) and everyone was in a total state of shock.

I got a shout on 4th August that turned out not to be a match (I am, however, still in touch with the girl that got it!) then on 7th

In hospital just before my heart transplant in 2013.

August I got a shout. This time it was a perfect match so I was told to call my family and prepare myself for surgery.

My wife and daughter came with me to surgery and were there as I was wheeled in. The next thing I remember was waking up in ICU feeling just on

Me and my friends; the Mayor and Mayoress of Gateshead, together with my Mam at Ryton Hirings, May 2014.

top of the world. The difference was absolutely immediate. I have to say at this point that all the staff at The Freeman, from cleaners to consultants, are some of the most dedicated, amazing people I have ever met.

My life is now utterly changed. I have stood as a candidate in the local elections for Gateshead Council. I have fulfilled a lifetime dream to fly in a helicopter and, most importantly, I am now a committee member of The Freeman Hospital Heart and Lung Transplant Association (FHLTA) and am going to take part in The Transplant Games in MY home town of Newcastle / Gateshead in July 2015.

I am hoping to raise as much money as I can for The Games and FHLTA. All this just over a year since I was told I only had a couple of months to live.

"I know it's an old trope, but, my life is so blessed. All because a family made a courageous and wonderful decision to donate their son's organs to save other's lives. Live Life, Give Life."

Tina's Story

Tina Stevens

On 5th May 2006 at Manchester Airport, just about to go into the car park and a pilot, driving a car slammed into us, really shook us up! Parked car, said we'll sort damage out after holiday. Not a good start.

First week of holiday in Altinkum, Turkey was great! – I had to go to a walk in clinic with pains in right neck and shoulder as I'd been bitten, they put me on a drip and it eased. The doctor visited 2 days running at my hotel to give me an antihistamine injection. I felt much better.

Second week of the holiday, Tuesday 16th May, I tried swimming which I loved and usually did a mile! I did one length and just about climbed out feeling weak and shattered! Very odd, I thought, went and had a shower ready for the belly dancing show later on.

The night was going well and we were all up dancing. I told my partner I didn't feel too good and went to the room to fetch a new film for the camera and for a breather. Not sure how I got back down but 2 minutes later I fled back to room stripping off clothes and jewellery as I went, I couldn't breathe and started to panic.

My partner raced to get the manager, I was still struggling to breathe and was really scared! The manager arrived, picked me up, put a dressing gown round me and ran out the hotel to a waiting car, he bundled me in the back and my partner jumped in next to me. Then, Bang! The most horrendous feeling, like I'd been shot in the middle of my back and dropped..........

At the local hospital they struggled to keep me flat as I was fighting to sit up then, Bang again...... This happened 3 times. All I remember hearing was the translator saying we need to inform her family she won't make this......

At this point, I'd had a cardiac arrest. My heart was so badly damaged by this and I was in congestive heart failure. The doctors couldn't believe, given my age, with my build and constant energy to keep fit and healthy, how this had come about.

I needed a heart transplant as soon as possible.

Talking was very difficult as was breathing, walking was a no go and I required a wheelchair. I had no energy as my heart was now barely functioning.

Friday 19th May, I woke up at 3am and politely threw up, the nurses rushed round my bed. I hadn't a clue where I was or how I got here.... Kusadassi 100km away. My partner George was looking in a tiny window and not allowed in, he was wearing the same clothes and looked dreadful. He must have had a terrible time.

Not sure on the date but near the middle / end June I got a fit to fly! Yay, I'm going home, I couldn't walk, eat or do anything I was so ill, they put me In the ambulance and drove me and George to Izmir, put us into a private Lear Jet to Istanbul, then another ambulance to the Ataturk Airport on the European side, met by Chris, a British Dr who flew over to get me home. I cried with relief. He looked at paperwork, X-rays and called the UK, he didn't want me to fly! The UK said to get me back ASAP! We boarded the flight, myself on first with oxygen etc, all going well then 1 hour into flight I had that .....Bang again.......

We were going to Manchester, the flight landed at Heathrow and I was taken, lights blaring to Harefield, they had no room, so I was rushed to Hillingdon where they did tests and straight away said I had approx. 6 hours to live. I thought: I've fought so far, I can again. Ten days later we were driven home to Cumbria, my car was already there from Manchester Airport, my sister and the AA recovered it, all battered.

I then spent the next year fighting to keep alive in and out on a weekly basis to hospitals.

October 2007, I had a transient ischaemic attack (TIA) or "mini stroke" which meant I couldn't have my Internal Cardiac Defibrillator fitted for 6 months; it was eventually fitted in April 2008.

11th June 2008 5am..... Phone rang.... "Hi it's Lynn Holt, how are you?" Shakily, I said I was ok. "We'll call in half an hour but get ready to get here quickly." I put the phone down and got my daughter up... OMG it's really happening, yes! I called George and he was at my house in record time. By 5:30 we were on our way to Newcastle, lights on full, at 7:30, 100 miles later, I was wheeled into theatre.......

Now I began a new life, it's a miracle and the selfless act of my donor's family to give me this precious part of their, mother, daughter, aunt, to keep safe as long as I can.

I've now seen my daughter go to Uni, graduate, get engaged, buy her first home and plan her wedding for August 2016; I'm making her cake.

Double Lung and Heart Transplant – 22nd February 2013

Amanda Henchliffe

My Condition:

I was born with a Coarctation of the Aorta. This was not corrected until I was aged 4. As a consequence, I developed Endocardial Fibroelastosis – a very rare condition. This was diagnosed during my nurse training when it was found that I had Severe Pulmonary Arterial Hypertension (high blood pressure in the lungs). The first of these causing severe damage to my heart – the heart muscle became very stiff with calcification (heart of stone!) causing the heart to remodel itself damaging the valves and chambers, this in turn caused severe back pressure of blood flow to the lungs, thus necessitating both heart and lung transplants. A very rare procedure now and only 4 of these operations were performed in the UK the year I had mine.

At the age of 26 I went into Atrial Fibrillation, ultimately requiring ablation of the AV node with full pacing support from a pacemaker (to give me a heartbeat). This was my Millennium present!!

Subsequent years found my symptoms gradually deteriorating with the onset of heart failure. This had a devastating effect on my family, friends and me. I had to stop being the outdoor, active type (gym every day before work), Mother, Wife, academic person (always trying to progress myself in my career) and gradually became dependent upon others for help with the most simple things. I had to stop my career as a Practice Nurse as I became too ill to be added to the transplant waiting list despite still managing to work 40 hours a week. THIS WAS ALL UTTERLY DEVASTATING!!!!!!!!!

My Life before Transplant:

I was very breathless, blue and cold (5 layers, central heating and open fire still not enough!) I suffered from Mesenteric Angina (gut not receiving blood supply, causing sudden extreme pain), I was constantly tired but unable to sleep, clinically depressed and very underweight. I had a pacemaker and a Hickman line feeding drugs directly into my heart, which also caused constant pain from the line in my chest to the outside syringe driver. I was sensitive to medication side effects (pain). I had to maintain a fluid restriction of 1 litre daily (5 tea cups), which included all drinks, milk for cereals, sauces, gravy etc. as I could put on a stone in fluid in less than a week. I became wheelchair bound. I suffered multiple acute kidney injuries (kidney failure requiring a kind of dialysis). I had several blood clots in my kidneys and spleen. I had to use oxygen therapy.

I had to retire from work due to ill health and was unable to travel. I suffered from social isolation – not being able to go out, meet with friends etc; had an ongoing effect on David (my husband) and Evan (our son), wider family and friends. The impact on their lives – needing to care for me meant foregoing any real life for themselves.

The Transplant:
I had my first call in August 2012. This was a false alarm so I was sent home. At the 2nd call in February 2013 we had the 999 ambulance dash to Newcastle. When the call came it felt very different to my false alarm call – I just knew this was it and I was initially frightened to go through with it but having David and Evan with me, I never doubted that it was the right thing for us. I was in theatre for 6 1/2 hours, going to ITU at approx 11.30 – 12 midnight. By 9am I was waking up, off

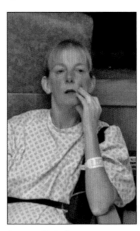

Immediately pre op-waiting for the trolley to take me to theatre for my transplant.

Post op Day 3: Amazing what a new heart and lungs can do for a girl!! Pink and shiny and new!

ventilation, my new organs fully supporting me. I was warm; in fact I felt hot and flushed. I could breathe and lie flat. I knew I had made it through. The staff who looked after me were absolutely tremendous, caring, supporting and encouraging. I was able to return home after 3 weeks!

Life after Transplant:
For my 1st Anniversary, I held a party in recognition of everyone who had supported us but mostly to acknowledge my donor family. We raised a little money for The Freeman Heart and Lung Transplant Association. Despite

a few little niggles, I am back at work as a senior nurse 30 hrs a week, pain free, I can breathe, I am warm, can eat / drink, am able to socialise. I take fewer tablets than before. With support, I am able to take part in physical activity, (I have climbed 2 UK mountains) and have increased my self-confidence, trying new skills like climbing. In 2014 I took part in my first British Transplant Games with several hundred other transplantees.

"I am alive and am positive about life and the future. My motto throughout has been "I will try" and I am hoping that this is fulfilling my part of the contract with my donor family and the team looking after me, helping to make the transplant process a success to inspire others."

Left: My medals and sheer thrill at taking part in my first Transplant Games in 2014.

On my ascent, Scafell Pike May 2015

A New Chapter of My Life

Lisa Shrive

My name is Lisa. I'm 46 years old and I had my transplant in January 2014 after suffering with chronic lung disease and failing heart. I was diagnosed at 35 with a condition called Sarcoidosis and although I did get out of breath I was still able to do many things like horse riding. When I got to my 40's I got diagnosed with not only Sarcoidosis, I'd got Emphysema. At the age of 43, my lungs started to collapse to the point half of one had to be removed and they glued it to my chest bone. I started to deteriorate so much that I had to sell my horse. I couldn't do any house work. My 8 year old daughter, Amy, became my carer. I was also then diagnosed with primary hypertension and was in desperate need of a transplant. My doctors gave me less than two years to live, if that.

In November 2013, I got a call but it was a false alarm and was then told I had less than a month left. And still I didn't believe I was dying. Christmas came and New Year; me, Amy and my nurse celebrated by watching the fireworks from my bed as I could no longer move. My breathing was so bad; I was on 15 litres of oxygen and on palliative care. On January 2nd, I was rushed into hospital and

Taken the day before my transplant when I was so near the end.

I thought 'this is the end,' plus I had had enough. I had no quality of life and I didn't want my daughter waking up and finding me gone. I was tired, too tired to continue. I had just said goodnight to my daughter from my room in the hospital when I got the call. They said they might have some lungs and it was looking good. I kept calm in the hospital, didn't want to get my hopes up after last time but so far so good. Things were looking good. At 11.37 on the 3rd of January I fell asleep to wake up a day later with new lungs.

The day after my transplant, the improvement was immediate.

I haven't stopped living ever since. I walk everywhere with my daughter, taking my dog, Derek, out.

Me with Amy, my daughter, a week post-transplant – going from strength to strength.

Me, back horse riding.

I'm back horse riding and for the first time in 14 years, we are off on holiday with friends; all 40 of us!

At my first transplant games, Bolton 2014.

"Thank you, Rona, for the new life you have given me."

NHS Organ Donor Register:
0300 123 23 23
www.organdonation.nhs.uk

My Journey to Heart Transplant

Barrie Braidford

My journey began on the day I was born, 2nd of December 1941, five days before the attack on Pearl Harbour but it was five years later, when I began school that the doctor doing my medical noticed the sounds he heard were indicative of leaking valves in my heart.

At that time, this was consistent with valve damage due to rheumatic fever and thereafter, every doctor who listened to my heart said that I must have had rheumatic fever. My mother always denied this and they used to say "It was during the war, you may have missed it." Mother always argued that I had never had rheumatic fever.

After living in South Africa for 7 years, where we went because my Dad got a job there working for The English Electric Company, we returned to Newcastle to live with my Grandma, in July 1953. We returned to England after my Dad died suddenly on the 5th of June 1953, three days after Coronation Day, at the ripe old age of 41. We think he died from a ruptured spleen as he had been playing football with the Natives on Coronation Day and had been struck very hard in the abdomen with a heavy old fashioned leather case ball.

During these years in Africa my heart was OK. In fact I played cricket and rugby while at boarding school.

It was now that another school medical resulted in me beginning to attend the cardiac unit at Newcastle General Hospital under the renowned cardiologist Dr Paul Szekely, who, incidentally died from a heart attack while being driven away from The Freeman by another consultant and although he was rushed back into the hospital they couldn't save him. Compared to today, the medical equipment was primitive, there was only one ECG machine in the North of England, operated by a Mrs Mangin, who guarded it jealously and wouldn't even let the Consultant touch it. Also, the radioactive screening took place in a darkened room; we [the patients] were all given a pair of red plastic goggles to wear. Each patient was then guided into a vertical cylinder made of some kind of Perspex which had openings on opposite sides. The consultant reached in through the openings and turned the patient around. Now we could all see everyone else's skeleton, it was entirely fascinating but a bit weird. Much later at The Freeman I was telling senior radiologist, Dr Mitchell about it and he said "Good God, they would be considered dangerous now!"

It was while attending these cardiac clinics that I first met Mr David Williams, Dr Szekelys registrar, who was to become Cardiac Consultant at The Freeman Hospital when it opened in 1978 and was to look after me until I first had my Mitral and Aortic valves replaced in 1981, with tissue valves, and then again in 1991 with mechanical valves when the tissue Mitral valve broke up. I almost died then. The first valve replacement was done on the National Health by the then, heart surgeon, Mr Blezovsky, now well retired.

After the first valve replacement, my original valves were sent for evaluation and it was decided that I had congenital valve damage; I had been born with leaking valves, nothing to do with rheumatic fever. Unfortunately my mother had died and never knew she had been right all the time.

The second valve replacement in 1991 was when I was a private patient as part of my salary included private health care [they didn't want me off work longer than necessary]. This time the surgeon was Mr Michael Holden, also now retired. He almost lost me this time and had to connect an inter-aortic balloon pump into my main artery in my right groin to help my heart to start beating again. I woke up in intensive care when I wasn't supposed to.

Incidentally, after the first valve job, I spent my 40th birthday in Ward 27. The nurses under Sister Brenda Hallams were fantastic as well as beautiful. They got me a cake and with the effects of that super-duper morphine, I thought I was in heaven with a bunch of Angels.

I was back at work again, I was now an Electrical/Instrumentation Supervisor in a chemical plant. It was a very physically and mentally demanding job and I had a breakdown in 1984, I was like a zombie for about three months but I was cajoled back to work by my Manager and the Human Resources Manager. I then plodded on until my heart began to fail big style in 1994; I actually phoned Dr Williams who happened to be on holiday on the Isle of Skye playing golf with retired surgeon Mr Blezsovsky, who now lived there. He rang me when he got back and told me to come and see him.

So, I went in and after a few quick tests; ECG, X-ray, echo, etc. he said "You cannot go back to work, I've done all that I can for you with valves and drugs, your only hope now is a heart transplant and I will make arrangements for you to meet the transplant team." "How will we manage financially?" I asked him and he said "Do not worry about that." I drove straight to my place of work and told my Manager I wasn't coming back to work. "Well you've got a sick note in for a fortnight," he said. "No I am never coming back" and I explained why.

"You can't do that to me!" he said. "What's this Doctors name?"

He then rang Dr Williams who put him in the picture and he eventually believed me. He then began singing my praises and said how much he had appreciated my input to his department, I got a bit emotional and began to cry; I had worked all of my life until then and frankly I was scared of the future. I had a wife and four children dependent on me. Next, I had a meeting with The Transplant Team and they agreed to put me on the list, warning me that I might have to wait some time because of the shortage of donor organs.

I now knew the co-ordinators, Lynn Holt and Neil Wrightson and had my pager. I had one false alarm when my pager went off only to be told that it must have been a passing Taxi or something that set it off as it wasn't them. Very disappointing after the excitement died down. Then in January 1996, I had an ischaemic stroke and my GP sent me straight to The Freeman for immediate admittance, however, there was a queue for beds and I was laid down on four chairs until one of the doctors on admittance found an empty bed on Ward 13, the diabetic ward at that time and everyone who went in there had a blood sugar test as a matter of routine. My blood sugar levels were "off the map" and they started injecting me with insulin immediately. I still inject insulin every day.

Then someone in Cardiac heard I was in and I was transferred to ward 24 in the Cardio block for my transplant assessment. A young doctor appeared at my bedside and I asked him what he did, to which he replied, "I am the Cardiologist that looks after you after your transplant."

"Oh!" said I, "I had better be nice to you then." That was my first encounter with Doctor Gareth Parry. I was then taken to the biopsy room where a team of young ladies poked things into and down my veins and measured the blood pressures in and around my heart to prove I was OK for transplantation.

I now had a new regime, as well as heart tablets I now had to measure blood sugar levels and inject insulin twice daily.

Then I arrived at transplant day, 26th November 1996, my sister's 52nd birthday. It was also the first time in my life that I was so poorly that I hadn't got out of bed; I could hardly talk let alone walk. At about 4:30pm my wife said to me "You've got to get up and go and see your Vivien as it's her birthday." So I dragged myself out of bed and went into the bathroom, got washed and was busy shaving when the phone rang at 4:50pm, it was Neil Wrightson. "Can you come in to talk about a transplant?" he said. I said I thought we had already talked about it at the meetings. "Yes but this time we've got a heart waiting for you, how soon can you get here?" "Twenty minutes," I said and off we went.

By 5:10pm, I was being shaved, chest and groin, by Neil and a nurse and was given my happy pill after signing the consent form. I was then wheeled merrily along to theatre, counting fluorescent tubes above me as I was wheeled along [once an electrician always an electrician]. I think it was a Tuesday evening into Wednesday that I had my heart transplant but I didn't wake up until Saturday afternoon, this time in a cubicle in 27A.

Unlike my previous valve jobs where I had been brought round in intensive care, I can vividly remember a 'hoover' tube out of my mouth and various other tubes and wires connecting me to the life support systems. It was on one of these occasions that I completely lost the plot. I suddenly thought, what a great place to bump somebody off, I mean who would question it and I decided they were trying to get rid of me. I started shouting that I needed to get out of there and started to try and remove some of the tubes. A young male nurse padded his back pocket, like the ASDA advert and said "Three hundred quid mate and I'll have you out of here." So I started yelling across the room to a young woman who was visiting, presumably a dying relative, as visitors are not usually allowed into intensive care. I was screaming at her to ring 2665275 [my then telephone number] to tell my wife to bring £300 for me urgently. I was then set upon by some older, more experienced nurses, one of whom actually climbed on to my bed, straddled me with her knees and grabbed both of my wrists to prevent me trying to pull any more tubes out, while others shoved the hoover tube [breathing tube] back into my throat to stop me shouting. They then sedated me again.

But back to ward 27A, post-transplant, as they woke me up, Match of the Day was just beginning and that well known tune; I was convinced that I was in the Kevin Keegan / Sir John Hall recuperation home for transplant patients. Then suddenly my wife and sons appeared climbing through the bushes to visit me. What bushes you may ask. That super-duper morphine again. That's now't that, after my other valve job I flew a Spitfire from an airfield in North Africa to defend Malta and was shot down just North East of Valetta harbour. Amazing stuff that morphine! Also, while recovering in 27A, I was visited by my mam and dad. Yeah really, although they had both been dead for years. Even now I cannot begin to explain it but at the time it seems so real that you believe it. Come with us my mam said, no more worries, no mortgage to pay, etc etc. Have I had any near death experiences, sure I have. Do I believe in life after death? Yes I do but I don't know why.

All of this preceding is why I am still alive and why I volunteered to be a FHLTA Committee Member, then Chairman of FHLTA, now back to Committee Member: to try in a very small way to help The Freeman Hospital Team and transplant recipients. While I was Chairman of FHLTA, I was privileged to have two tours of The Transplant Institute with the Project Engineer in charge while it was being built and to get to know Professor John Dark.

Coming Home Alone

Jack Atkinson

written by his father, David Atkinson

> My son Jack had a heart transplant at The Freeman in 2004, aged 13 months. This story describes a visit home while Jack was still waiting for his transplant.

The house was cold, cold as an undertaker's smile. It had been empty for a few weeks now and the chill in the bricks and mortar would take a while to shake. I turned the thermostat up to 28 and the boiler sparked to life. I knew that it didn't matter, 22, 25, 28, it wouldn't heat the house up any quicker. But I took some comfort from the thought it might. But worse than the cold was the silence.

I breathed in stale, dusty air. They say that eighty percent of dust comes from human skin, but if the house was empty where had all the dust come from? Perhaps it had been just hanging in the air and in the stillness had settled downward. It had gathered together in little clumps as if to avoid loneliness, and swirled in the eddies of my wake, still clinging together, dust to dust.

I went into the kitchen to make a cup of tea, to warm myself up from the inside out. The cloying smell of rotting food grabbed me and drew my eyes towards the pedal bin. I opened the fridge. The light flicked on, welcoming, spotlighting its contents, two chicken breasts, still in their supermarket packaging, going white and opaque in the centre and beginning to blacken around the edges, a bag of mixed leaf salad with bubbles of condensation on the inside, and a milk bottle, half full, with great yellow clots floating near the top. My tea was going to be black or none at all.

I opened both windows and closed the kitchen door, the bin and the fridge could wait. The door opposite had a little enamel sign proclaiming the entrance to Jack's room. It may as well have been a danger sign warning against high voltage, or radioactivity, or hungry animals with sharp teeth. I didn't want to open it but knew I must. Inside was perfectly preserved. I could still see the indentation of Jack's little body in the mattress of the cot. Around the hollow where his head had lain, here and there, were little

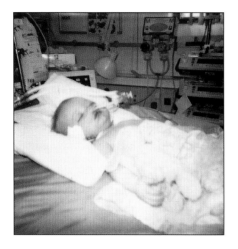

blonde hairs. She had told me not to touch anything, particularly the bedding. If she had nothing else at least she would still have his smell. But in time smells fade and drift away like ghosts and as more time passes memories slip away too until all you have left is an indentation.

His Winnie the Pooh mobile hung over the cot, guarding it until he returned. On the floor, his little "lellow" and blue car was parked at a strange angle, as if its driver had been in a rush and abandoned it. "Lellow" was his favourite colour.

From the top of the drawers, six pairs of button bear eyes stared at me accusingly. The drawers were open and the clothes inside were no longer neatly folded. They had been scattered during the hurried packing. She had gone with Jack in the ambulance, with the police escort. She had assumed such escorts were normal practice when transferring patients. I knew that it was not and had packed his clothes in a hurry. As it turned out the packing had been unnecessary.

Beside the cot was a small cardboard book, "Baby's First Book". I opened it. Page one, telephone – ring, ring; page two, keys – jingle jangle, page three... I closed it, switched out the light and pulled the door behind me.

In the living room toys were scattered on the floor. I stepped over them to the pine dresser and opened a drawer. I took out a photo album with a bright yellow Tweetie Pie on the front screaming "I tawt I taw a puddy cat". I settled down with it into my favourite armchair and opened it with the reverence reserved for an antique book. Inside were pictures of the day he was born and his first Christmas and every month between. The Christmas pictures were the last ones filed. His first birthday pictures were still in the camera, undeveloped. After lingering over each picture I carefully put them back, satisfied I had passed the test.

In the same drawer was a camcorder. I took it out, more confident now, switched it on, wound the tape back and pressed play. From the tiny screen a smile and a voice and a laugh reached out through time and touched me. I switched it off.

The house had begun to warm up, but seemed more silent than ever. I did the only thing I could think of to break the silence.

I cried.

"Jack is 12 now. We treasure every day."

Blue Baby to Pink Lady

Louise McLellan

Born in 1970 with a complex congenital heart disorder I had limitations, often having to sit out of P.E. lessons and watch the annual sports day from the sidelines. Following university I worked in Norfolk and it was here that my health started to deteriorate. This resulted in my having a TCPC (total cavopulmonary connection) at Royal Brompton Hospital in London in 1995. Over the next decade or so there followed several blue light incidents to A&E. In 2001 we moved to the North East and in 2008 I had another open heart procedure at The Freeman Hospital. Life hadn't been all bad though because in 2006 we adopted a beautiful baby girl, undoubtedly one of the best days of my life. It was for this gorgeous baby I so wanted to be well. Following a series of other operations and near death rhythm problems, I was informed that transplant was now my only option. I knew this but actually hearing my consultant say the words was hard to take in. Months later I found myself in hospital again for a transplant assessment and after three anxious days I was told that I was suitable and would be listed shortly. Some months passed and my health was declining. I had very little energy, could only walk at a snail's pace and was living nervous of being alone at any time with my little girl and going into a life threatening rhythm. During what had now become a regular visit to hospital for IV drugs, I was told my results were showing that my heart and other organs were failing. I was then admitted, put on the urgent transplant list and was to wait there on IV Milrinone which would help the heart until a new one became available.

The Freeman Hospital, Ward 24, was now my home. Six weeks later at 2am on 16th October 2013, I was awoken as a heart was available and I was the standby! I then lay awake thinking about the poor family, currently sitting by the bed of their loved one having given the go ahead to donate their organs. Morning arrived and after being prepared for theatre just in case, I was, at 11.30am, informed that the first candidate for this 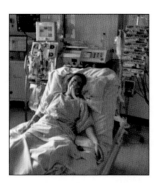 heart was not a match. A mixture of relief for myself, sorrow for the other patient and panic suddenly hit. At 12.30pm, following an emotional farewell to my husband, I walked into theatre. The first thing that hit me was the amount of equipment and the by-pass machine that I knew would soon be keeping me alive. After a fortnight in Intensive Care and a fortnight on Ward 38, I returned to my little girl and family having been separated for the longest and most surreal ten weeks of my life.

Seventeen months on, I feel like Wonder Woman, nothing can stop this new heart. On my last day on Ward 38, I wrote a goal to run the Great North Run in 2015, I am currently on track to do that for FHLTA. I exercise 6 days a week and love every minute. I bought a bike to ride with my family, am looking forward to my first Transplant Games in July and most importantly, I am now confident that I will be able to see my gorgeous daughter become an adult.

"A day never passes where I don't think about my wonderful donor and their truly amazing family for their bravery in those early hours of 16th October 2013 and of course I am forever grateful for the expertise and dedication of all The Freeman Team of Staff."

16 Years and Counting

Vicky Pettersen

A life I never thought I would be living,
A dream year I never thought I would see,
The gift that keeps on giving,
My Donor family consented,
And It came to me...

As we live our lives and do the things that other families do, we look very normal, very much like the next family in the street but unlike most families we are very thankful because I owe my life to someone we don't know, my Donor family, who made the decision to consent to their family member's organs being donated, for allowing it to be possible for me to live.

My husband Erik, myself and our son Antony celebrating our 25th wedding anniversary in 2015, 16 years post double lung transplant.

As with anyone born with Cystic Fibrosis our journey has had many significant moments where I came though the difficult times but none so much as when we needed to consider my going on the transplant list.

I was fortunate to have a good quality of life as a child and young adult with CF, my Dad had spoken to me when I was young about the possibility of us looking into transplantation when I was older and my health deteriorated. He had encouraged me to do running as a young teenager and felt the advantages of exercise for CF needed to be promoted more. Unfortunately, my Dad died when I was 17 from a brain tumour, which devastated me. This seemed to coincide with the start of my deterioration.

In 1988, aged 18, I ran The Great North Run non-stop with Erik but 18 months later when I got married in 1990, I was no longer able to run because of the deterioration in my chest condition.

In 1994, Erik and I went on to have our son, Antony. With a lot of family support we managed to go along with our life as normal as we could, although I did struggle physically.

By the time Antony was nearly five my lungs had deteriorated so much that I was on permanent oxygen and intravenous drugs and had no quality of life. To us, the decision about me going on the transplant list was made easier by knowing without it Antony definitely wouldn't have a Mum to turn to while he was growing up.

"The main thought in my mind was he is only 4 and won't have any memories of me if I die now."

I was sent up for transplant assessment at Freeman in November 1998 and after tests and discussion with the doctors it was decided it was time for me to go on the list for a double lung transplant.

Without hesitation I was put on the list. I in no way mean we didn't have lots of emotions and apprehensions about this. I was frightened, but the thought of leaving Antony and my wonderful Husband, Erik, more than frightened me; it terrified me. So much so that I could feel like I was suffocating and feel severe anxiety when I let the thoughts wonder into my mind.

These fears were helped with me receiving psychological assistance and by us being hopeful that the transplant could be the chance of a new life we were desperate for.

We tried to keep very positive about the prospect of a transplant and the chance of me receiving the call.

After one false call in March we came home devastated, not knowing if that had been my chance, terrified that we would not get the chance again. My emotions came down with a crash.

Thankfully less than four weeks later the call came again on 6th April 1999.

We arrived at the hospital at 7pm, were told it was a go ahead at 11.30pm and I was down in surgery by midnight. My transplant date was recorded as 7th April.

I woke up fully the next day at 3.00pm, had my ventilator out that evening and moved to the ward the next day.

I was fortunate to be home from the hospital 2 weeks and 5 days later and our new life began.

It still amazes me what our bodies can endure and recover from; how fast I recovered, how faithful my body has been to me, no matter what was thrown

With my son Antony in the transplant flats at the Freeman, on the day I was going home.

"My transplant allowed me to fulfil all my personal and my family's dreams."

at it through all the years of suffering with CF and later after the transplant, once I was diagnosed with chronic rejection 10 years later. Yet it still continues to be faithful regardless.

I watched my son grow from a 5 year old boy into a man and go off to University in London to study Music, all while being able to take an active part in his life. We created memories as a family, travelling Europe, spending special times together.

I fulfilled my dreams to be an independent person, mother and wife.

Erik and I celebrated our 25th Wedding Anniversary in March 2015 and as a family we celebrated our son's 21st Birthday in January.

We never imagined any of this was possible post-transplant, we hoped for a few years, maybe five if we were very lucky but didn't realise what we had was achievable.

I had a large drop in lung function after the first year which put me back to the results pre transplant. It looked like this could be the end for us. Erik and I talked and even then we agreed the transplant was still the best decision we had made as it had given us a wonderful year together as a family. Thankfully I was given a course of radiation and after a very tough 6 months my results started to increase back up.

I went on to have a further 9 years problem free until I reached my tenth year where I was diagnosed with chronic rejection. This meant a large drop in lung function again but thankfully it stabilized around 50 %. Even with the negative aspects of rejection I manage to live a wonderful life. I am still able to do the things I want in between the ups and downs experiences.

Our 25th wedding anniversary party.

I also have achieved many personal goals. I have spent 11 years volunteering with family support organisations and the last 4 years I have been actively involved in The Freeman Heart and Lung Transplant Association, first as a committee member and web site editor then the last 20 months as their Sports Manager.

This is a job I love. I feel like I was born to do this job. I have contributed to the team growing from 22 members at the games in Sheffield 2013 to 68 competitors for the upcoming games in Newcastle / Gateshead for 2015.

The FHLTA team have become our second family; we laugh, cry and celebrate together through all our amazing experiences.

In 2014, I competed in The European Heart and Lung Transplant Games in Vilnius, Lithuania by taking part in the 20k Cycle race, the 100m, the 800m and the Duathlon. We had a wonderful time and aim to go to The European Games next year, in 2016, to Finland.

I have also organised numerous events for Transplant Sport with the support of Erik.

I spend a lot of my time trying to keep fit and exercising, through walking and cycling.

Exercise is the one thing that makes me feel more alive than anything. I get a great satisfaction after completing something I have set out to do. It makes me feel thankful to be alive every time. I try to get people involved in some type of exercise post-transplant, while encouraging them to join the team. I throw myself 100% into everything I do. Taking part in The British Transplant Games gives me a great sense of achievement and I meet some inspiring people who have become friends for life. It gives me motivation to train through the year.

As a young girl I was a county cross country runner and although in my head I would still like to be that person, I have settled with the lower level I am at and enjoy the fact that I am still able to take part in events, no matter what my ability is.

As a youngster I used to holiday in the Lakes and walked up Helvellyn.It was a life goal of mine to return to the mountains In the lakes one day and I honestly thought my chance had gone with the decline in my lung function. I was very proud to climb up Skiddaw in Keswick (3053ft) via Ullock Pike and Long side edge in September 2015 with Erik for the celebration of our Silver Wedding. It was very frightening near the edge close to the top but I got a great sense of personal achievement when I reached the summit at 16 years post double Lung transplant. It was a wonderful, proud and emotional moment for myself and Erik to celebrate together.

I spend a lot of my free time promoting Organ Donation with the hope that more people will sign the Organ Donation Register to hopefully give more families like mine the chance to survive and flourish.

I love my life, I thank God every day that I am still here to live it and share it with my wonderful family. My next personal goal is to see my son graduate next year in London from the music course he is completing and go out into the world as an independent person. God willing, I will be there by his and Erik's side while celebrating Antony's Graduation, together.

I must thank my amazing husband who is my soul mate and best friend. Our Son Antony is our reason for everything we do. He is the light in our life.

I also want to thank our extended family and friends for everything they have done to support myself and my family through our journey. Without them it would not have been as successful.

"My Donor family and Helen, my donor, are always in my thoughts."

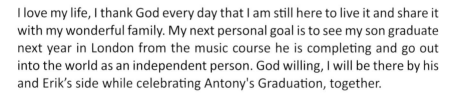

NHS Organ Donor Register:
0300 123 23 23
www.organdonation.nhs.uk

A Different Perspective

Vicky Pettersen

Written by Erik Pettersen

I've known my wife now for 28 years, a number in our wildest dreams we never thought would have been possible. I will say life has never always been easy and we have had our high and low points along the roller coaster of our transplant journey.

I first met my wife to be on Christmas Eve in 1987, I was basically owed £5 for tickets to the local nightclub, Vicky happened to be one of the young ladies that wanted one. Even then it took 3 months to finally get her to go out with me!

Vicky was born with CF and diagnosed at 3 years old. Back then in the 70's living into your teens was considered an achievement. On our transplant journey I believe there are a few reasons why life has turned out for our family the way it has. Firstly there was Vicky's dad, Stan. I'm saddened to say I never really met Stan as he died in the February before we started dating. He has had a massive impact on my wife's life from an early age getting her into sport and keeping fit, one thing he also spoke about was that sometime in the future transplant would be a plausible option in her fight against her CF. This was a dad speaking to his daughter in the 80's about transplant and its benefits. The Freeman didn't start its Lung Transplant programme until 1990. I'm certain when our time came about transplant being the next stage in Vicky's treatment this made a difficult decision a little easier due to his vision.

Vicky was in very good health when we first met, a county cross country runner. We even ran the Great North run in 1988 together in just over 2 hrs, within a year though the hospital admissions started. Looking back the treatment was poor and my brother in law Stan, a newly trained Doctor, managed to get Vicky transferred to the regional CF unit in Leeds under the guidance of Steve Conway and his team. By now Vicky had already been for transplant referral via Middlesbrough and was actually on the active list. Things were very different in Leeds. The care, the treatment, the host of specialist people to help in the management of my wife's CF and 8 weeks later my wife was taken off the active list at Freeman as she had made a remarkable recovery and had never been in better health after a pretty poor 2 years. It was in Seacroft Hospital, Leeds, where we met other people with CF and even a few who had also received transplants. One person in particular, Paul, recently transplanted back then and still here 23 years later. He inspires us both about what transplant can bring.

Within a further 2 months to our surprise and Steve Conway's – her CF Consultant, Vicky was pregnant. I can still vividly recall Steve walking across the car park not looking best pleased as another of his CF ladies had become pregnant. A bit earlier than planned our son Antony Stanley James arrived. It's all we called Vicky's bump. In fact we didn't have a girl's name in mind. The midwife even asked what names we had chosen to which we replied just Antony! Looking back at the earlier years in particular from such good health to being on the transplant programme in just 2 years was all just pretty normal existence, routine and regime. Looking from the outside it must have been a real slog and I guess we didn't realise just how unwell and challenging our lives had become.

Antony's arrival certainly changed everything on our transplant journey and I'm certain that having a child to now consider added more of the determination and desire instilled by Vic's dad Stan.

Not only was I Vicky's main carer with treatment and help, I was now Antony's too. We always tried to do things as a family but as Vicky's health got worse I found myself doing more and more of the family stuff with our son on my own.

When Antony was 4 ½ the transplant process started again at the Freeman, this time it felt like we were in control and it was a decision made by ourselves to look at the possibility of a transplant.

Antony's 18th Birthday.

Vicky went active on the list in the December of 1998. We knew the wait could be 18 months if the call even came. We consider ourselves lucky. We had one false call in the March which at the time you do think you have missed the opportunity and the call will never come.

On April 6th 1999 I was on my way home from work to be greeted by Vicky at the door, transplant bag in hand. Neil had called with the possibility of some lungs being available that evening. Off we went. Antony was actually out with his grandma so Vicky didn't get to say goodbye. When he returned home, he was just told, "Mam's gone for her new lungs," by Grandma and off he went. Five year olds make the process sound so simple and easy.

So April 6th sat in the Freeman, it kind of felt right as if this was our opportunity to get the transplant that would transform our family life.

Now Vicky was always very positive about transplant and if she had any fear it certainly didn't show, not until 11.55pm on the trolley before going into theatre where she started going into an anxiety attack, then we went into the pre theatre room together.

Six hours or so later we had a call from Prof Dark to say operation was all done and that Vicky would be in ICU in the hour. By the afternoon Vicky was awake, writing instructions to the family, then 2 hours later the tubes were out. She was moved the following morning onto Ward 27A. Within three days the exercise bike was in the room after 2 weeks

Vicky with her Surgeon, Professor John Dark.

and 5 days we were back home in New Marske. This recovery isn't really the norm and we know of many friends who have struggled and fought hard to come through their own transplant experience although I'm sure they all would tell you it was worth it.

It was once we got home being back to a normal family with a young child, not dependent on 24 hour oxygen and care, all the things most of us take for granted, we could now all share life together.

Looking back I had become tired, bad tempered and frustrated whilst seemingly having a normal life albeit working full time. Treatments morning and night and a young son requiring your time and attention took its toll. I hadn't really realised this at the time.

Now we could start crossing off things to do, that to most people would be considered very normal. It started with Birthdays with Antony, going to different schools, GCSE's, going to college, A-levels and getting into University. Our son Antony is 21 now, who knew; when he was 5 just getting a few extra years from a transplant we thought would have been amazing.

Me and Vicky at the European Heart & Lung Transplant Games, Vilnius Lithuania, 2014.

Vicky always said she would like to renew her vows at 20 years. At the time I think we both thought this really might not happen. I actually organised this as a surprise, well up to 2 weeks before, when the vicar suggested I tell Vicky so she could get a new dress. We have now just celebrated our 25th wedding anniversary together.

Vicky has also managed to get back into her sport, albeit at a much lower level than in her teens. She has won medals at transplant games both in the UK and Europe. One thing I can say is, it isn't about winning, more that you can take part and enjoy whatever sport you enter.

All this is thanks to a lady; Helen and her family, 16 years ago whilst we were at the Freeman hoping for a better future for our family they managed to consent to organ donation in what must have been a very sad time for their family. Helen sadly died suddenly from a brain haemorrhage. This unbelievable act of courage, kindness, call it what you want has allowed our family to have a different future and for that we will be forever grateful.

Let me add, for all the joy and happiness the transplant has given our family it hasn't always been easy; acute rejection after 1 year requiring Total Lymphoid Irradiation (TLI), and 5 years ago, chronic rejection. Vicky's lung function isn't what it was, although it doesn't stop us from doing or achieving anything.

We are still currently on board the transplant roller coaster of life and enjoying it every day. We have met some fantastic people who we call our transplant family, they all have similar tales to tell and stories to share.

I think the biggest hurdle to transplant is fear of what may lie ahead. Transplant isn't for everyone and sometimes doesn't work , I have seen this first hand through the years but what I will say is anyone thinking of or currently going through the transplant process is go for it, you will be on an amazing journey. Not easy by any means, but worth every minute.

NHS Organ Donor Register:
0300 123 23 23
www.organdonation.nhs.uk

Two Stories, One Donor

Gill Hollis

A few years ago I attended a wedding with my husband, Peter. It was a family wedding, of sorts. I don't know if there is a term that describes the relationship of the bride, Susie, to me – but we are related.

One night in February 2004, Susie and I received life-saving transplant operations. Susie received the heart and I received a lung from the same donor and that continues to be a very special bond.

My lung problems began in 1987 when I was in my early twenties. I'd always been fit and healthy but soon after returning home from a trip, trekking in The Himalayas, my right lung collapsed. Five years and several lung collapses later, I was diagnosed with a very rare disease, Lymphangioleiomyomatosis (now known as LAM). I was told that my prognosis was uncertain but that there was no treatment and no cure.

It was a devastating diagnosis. At the time, in 1992, lung transplants were still very new; certainly, a transplant wasn't presented as an option for me then. So it was only in 1996, as I was about to undergo more lung surgery, that the possibility of a lung transplant was first mentioned to me. Now I know, that for some people, being told you might need a transplant will have been terrifying news. But I was really excited because for the first time since my diagnosis, I was given that very precious thing – hope! Hope that my future might hold something other than the ultimately terminal march of the disease.

In the meantime, though, I was being forced to give up my favourite activities one by one and as my world shrank, so did that of my family because we couldn't do anything together. By summer 2003, I was on oxygen 24 hours a day, eating and sleeping were difficult and showering and dressing in the morning took hours. I'm naturally an energetic and sociable person but was unable to be either.

I was finally put on the transplant list in July 2003. By then, my physical symptoms were at least matched by the psychological impact of my situation; I was deteriorating rapidly and was terrified that my call would not come in time.

It was a difficult time but we soon realised that, at The Freeman, I was being cared for by the most professional, experienced and lovely set of people. Everyone was so matter-of-fact and they all, from the porter who whizzed me around in my wheelchair, through to the most senior of the medical team, talked as if having a transplant was the most normal thing in the world. They oozed expertise and genuine warmth, which was so reassuring.

I was lucky. In February 2004, I was called to The Freeman that same night as Susie, to receive the transplant that would save my life.

Susie (left) and me at the FHLTA 30th Anniversary dinner, May 2014

Since then, in general, life has been good! Of course, there have been setbacks but the benefits have far outweighed them. My quality of life is excellent. It is wonderful to live a normal life again: spending time with friends and family, working, playing sport and I've had some memorable holidays too; teaching my nephews to ski and sea-kayak, cycling 300km down the Danube to Vienna and completing two of New Zealand's multi-day walks. In summary, I am a participant again rather than a frustrated spectator.

"I still think my transplant is an absolute miracle and I owe so much to the miracle workers of The Freeman and, of course, to my donor, the donor I share with Susie."

My Story

Susie Wood

For me, growing up with a congenital heart defect was a tricky business. Walking in the wind, climbing stairs and staying warm were all a challenge but I had nothing to compare my experience to. It was my life and I enjoyed it. I am immensely grateful to the surgeons at The Brompton Hospital who helped me to survive the first 27 years of my life. Despite my limitations, I completed school, attended university in York and qualified as an Occupational Therapist in 1998.

My transplant journey began in 2003 when I collapsed at work and was admitted to an ITU ward that I had been working on the previous day. My concerned colleagues at James Cook Hospital wondered where to begin; their Freeman equivalents said simply, "Get her here safely and we will take it from there," which is exactly what happened.

Dr O'Sullivan said to me that I had effectively been rowing all of my life. A transplant would, he said; provide me with an "outboard motor."

My transplant took place on a cold and very windy evening in February 2004. I didn't know it at the time but my donor gave two wonderful gifts that night. Gill Hollis and I share a remarkable bond – we share our donor.

My aim, since my transplant, has been, in the words of Katherine Mansfield, to "become all that I am capable of becoming". I became involved in the transplant games and have benefitted hugely from the friendship and support of team members. I have been able to complete my Masters degree and go trekking in Iceland (both long held ambitions).

I have completed the Great North Run 4 times now, walked Hadrian's Wall and scaled Snowdon. These are achievements beyond my wildest pre transplant imaginings.

My amazing parents have provided care and encouragement throughout my journey and my lovely husband, Mark, gives his own brand of Yorkshire advice "If you want to do it, just get on with it."

During my time editing the FHLTA website, I came across a quote. It is from John Brasher, co – founder of the London Marathon. It relates to the running fraternity but has resonance for my extended Freeman family too. He talked of the importance of "One joyous family, working together, laughing together; achieving the impossible."

Me, my husband Mark and Rex, out walking near Guisborough.

"I am so very grateful to my unknown donor, who allows me, every day, to achieve the impossible. This story is dedicated to them."

NHS Organ Donor Register:
0300 123 23 23
www.organdonation.nhs.uk

Live Every Day as if it's Your Last

Joanne Hope

When I was born I had only half my heart working. I was ok until I was 3 when I started to black out and collapse. It was then I got my first pacemaker. I was always tired and "blue" growing up and some kids at school could be mean to me. I just let it go over my head. I can remember being 7 years old and swimming with the school. It was June time and I felt really, really cold. I remember the teacher telling me to go and get my clothes on. She came into the changing rooms and felt my head and she said "You are warm. We don't like little girls and boys who lie." That night I was rushed into Freeman Hospital. It turned out that I had Cardiomyopathy and my lungs were filling up with blood. Basically I was drowning in my own blood. It was around that time that my parents were told I would need a heart transplant in the future. At aged 10 I received a second pacemaker and that was when my parents were told I definitely needed a new heart. A few months later, a friend of mine had his new heart and when I went to see him, that's when my parents dropped the bombshell that I needed one too. It felt surreal to be told.

I was put on the active list in July 1989. I always remember it was 4:30pm on a Monday when we were told. At 10am the next morning all the kids at school were running round looking for me. My mam was in the office..... I had a call for a heart. I was taken to theatre and woke up on a ventilator. They had prepared me for the op but found out the heart was too badly bruised so it couldn't be used.

On the 20th August 1989 (2 days after my 12th birthday), I was at my uncle's house in Billingham with my mam and brother when my dad called to say there was a call for me. I ended up getting a police escort to Freeman. I felt like The Queen, they even closed the Tyne tunnel for me!! Sadly that heart was too big. I can remember 4th October sat with my dad and brother watching Top Gun. My mam was at a Tupperware party at a neighbour's house. My dad made us crispy bacon and sausages and he said to me; "When you have your transplant you won't be able to eat these." I just laughed. I went to bed about 10pm and heard the phone ring... for some reason I just knew it was for me... I looked out of my bedroom window and saw my dad run over for my mam.

At 5am on the 5th October 1989, I went down for my transplant. This time it was successful. What I didn't know is that my parents had been told I had 2 weeks to live, at most, had I not had the call when I did.

I remember waking up. Looking at my legs and saying that they were fat!! I came out of intensive care after 3 days and was put in isolation in Ward 23 for a week. After that there was no stopping me!! I used to ride a bike up and down the ward. I'd never been able to do that before. Three weeks and one day to the day I was done, I went home.

For Christmas that year I asked for a bike. I'd never, ever owned one before. I went from strength to strength and went back to school. I went on an aeroplane for the first time. I left school then went on to college.

When I was 17, I fell pregnant. At the time, transplant pregnancies weren't really heard of but I was determined I was going to have it. I gave birth on 27th July 1995, 3 weeks early (he was due on my 18th birthday), to a healthy 5lb 7oz son, who I called Luke.

Me and Baby Luke. In the year this book comes out, 2015, Luke will have turned 20.

In the past 26 years I have done lots of amazing things:

- Left school and college
- Learned to ride a bike
- Passed my test
- Travelled the world
- Swam with dolphins
- Found alcohol (lol)
- Had rods put either side of my spine due to scoliosis
- Got engaged and married to a wonderful man called Ian
- Learned to be a hairdresser / beautician / masseuse / reflexologist / nail technician.

I am currently waiting for a kidney transplant. I'm on dialysis 3 times a week.

I also work full time at a job I love! I work as a chat moderator for Tombola. It's the best job ever!!!

I would like to thank my donor's family for their selfless act of donating their child's organs; without them I wouldn't be here. And neither would Luke.

"I urge everyone to become an organ donor. My motto is 'You can't use your organs when you die... So give them to someone else for the chance to live.'"

My Story

Joan Whitney

Following an undiagnosed heart attack in 1996, I went into severe heart failure, unable to walk very far, I had continuous breathing problems and the only solution suggested by my Cardiologist was a heart transplant.

I was referred to the wonderful Freeman Hospital, Newcastle-upon-Tyne for an assessment. The outcome of the assessment, which lasted 3 days and involved various tests and meetings with Consultants, Doctors, Nurses, and a Social Worker, was in me being placed on the active transplant list. Six weeks later in 1997, I was fortunate to receive the Gift of Life.

After being so poorly for months with heart failure, then receiving my new heart, which made me feel so well immediately, I couldn't believe I could breathe so normally. I then had to build up my strength and fitness to cope with life.

Following my recovery, my co-ordinator at The Freeman Hospital started talking about competing in The British Transplant Games and taking up sport again – it felt a large mountain to climb considering I had not been able to exercise for a long time. It was suggested I went to a Transplant Badminton Tournament, which I did and was so inspired by the fitness of the competitors, I thought 'I can do that,' and that was the start of my interest in the Sports-side of Transplantation.

I entered the next Badminton Tournament and was selected to go to Japan for The World Games, which was one of the many exciting places I have visited since my Transplant. It is a very special thing to do, not only competing in sport which shows what can be achieved following a Transplant and raising awareness of Organ Donation, but to meet so many different people from all walks of life who have received the "Gift of Life" be it a Heart, Heart/Lung, Lungs, Liver, Kidney, Bone Marrow, we feel this special bond with each other, knowing none of this would be possible without the generosity of our donors and their families.

In 2001, I joined the Freeman Heart & Lung Transplant Association committee, which is an organisation that supports members who have received a heart, heart and lung transplant or double lung transplant at The Freeman Hospital. In 2003, I became Treasurer of the FHLTA, a post which I held until 2014.

I try and keep healthy, continue working as a committee member for the FHLTA and enjoying my family which includes 8 grandchildren. Hopefully I will be in Liverpool for the 2016 British Transplant Games and in Vantaa (Helsinki) for the 2016 European Championships. I am the oldest member of The Freeman sports team!

All this has happened in the past 18 years due to the enormous generosity of a family who sadly lost their loved one but chose to donate her organs.

I have had many new adventures, met some wonderful people of all ages and backgrounds, there have been a few ups and down, sadly my husband died 7 years ago. The whole Transplant experience has been very humbling – I have been one of the fortunate people who received the ultimate gift –

"THE GIFT OF LIFE"

At the opening parade of the European Heart and Lung Championships, Vilnius, Lithuania 2014.

With two of my 8 grandchildren.

NHS Organ Donor Register:
0300 123 23 23
www.organdonation.nhs.uk

Liam's Transplant Story

Liam Waterworth

I was born with Pulmonary Atresia, which is a complex congenital heart defect so I was restricted from doing normal everyday things in life. I had numerous operations throughout my life and this resulted in me having a heart transplant on 26/03/2013.

I never gave a heart transplant a thought until I deteriorated in 2012, then it was suggested by my consultant to give it serious thought as my heart was gradually deteriorating.

I went home with mixed emotions, thinking of living life with a healthy heart, doing all the things that I would be able to do but having a fear of having a heart transplant. After serious thought and being admitted to hospital once again, I knew now that this was my only hope of a healthy normal life. This decision was very difficult as I knew the risks and my future was unpredictable at this time.

I was then admitted to The Freeman Hospital for transplant assessment. It was good news; I was a suitable candidate for a new heart. This was my 1st hurdle over. Whilst in The Freeman I was able to speak to people who had been on this journey, this inspired me to keep going, I then made the decision to stay at Freeman and await a new heart.

The next few weeks consisted of many assessments and procedures, one of which was being attached to a continuous drip of Milnrone. This meant 24 hours a day sat on Ward 24 awaiting a new suitable heart.

Three weeks later I got the call that I had been waiting for, it was 9 o'clock on 25th March 2013 that a suitable heart was available. That night was a blur as I was in shock. It was all happening so fast. I had mixed emotions once again, all the medical staff & coordinators reassured me that this was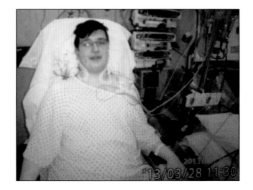

what I had been waiting for. My Mum, who was with me, contacted my family who travelled up to be with me.

As I was wheeled down to theatre I knew now there was no turning back. I had a goal to fulfil, my sister was getting married in Cyprus in 6 months and my wish was to be at my sister's wedding with a healthy new heart.

I woke up to feel this pounding sensation in my chest then I knew that all gone well, looking around at the monitor and seeing a steady heart beat and oxygen levels at a 100% was the best feeling in the world. I made a steady recovery. I just took things day by day, as there may be hiccups along the way. I had kidney failure that lasted approximately 12 weeks. This kept me and my Mum at the hospital, we lived in a flat provided by Freeman on site.

The day came when I was allowed home, I was eventually weeing again and not needing dialysis.

My goal of being at my sister's wedding was achieved and I had a better quality of life to look forward to.

Since having my transplant I have achieved many other goals which include representing The Freeman in The Transplant Games, holidays abroad and fishing in France. In 2015, in one of the leagues, I competed in a semi-final match. In another league I competed in a final match in my snooker club and got 3 trophies. This was a massive achievement for me. I also won Gold playing snooker at The British Transplant Games in 2015.

I am looking forward to living life to the full and would like to thank the magnificent team at The Freeman Hospital for everything they have done for me.

By the way, I got a dog that I always wanted and called him Hassan!!

In Our Hearts

Liam Waterworth

We thought of you today.

But that is nothing new.

We thought about you yesterday.

And days before that too.

We think of you in silence.

We often speak your name.

Now all we have are memories.

And your picture in a frame.

Your memory is our keepsake.

With which we'll never part.

God has you in his keeping.

I have you in our heart.

Breath of Life

Mark Allen

I was born with Cystic Fibrosis, but I was a pretty healthy child. In fact, I was in my late 20's when I was in hospital overnight for the first time. I grew up in Cannock Wood in Staffordshire and played for the local football and table tennis teams, played badminton once a week and was a member of the newly formed Cannock Wood Cricket Club.

During university (I studied politics in Manchester) I got to spend a year in Holland and from then the travel bug took hold. I travelled widely, whenever I could. I spent the next summer in the USA working on a Salvation Army camp for kids and then went travelling with a friend, who is a sister of the very lovely Natalie Imbruglia.

I became a journalist and worked my way up to The Express and Star. I got to interview Tony Blair, ride in a tank covering the troubles in Northern Ireland and chat to the rich and famous as well as sit through boring council meetings. You had to be tough. People tend to hate journalists (usually only those with something to hide) and you are not well paid for the stick you take. But it is a vocation....

I moved to Australia in 1999 to experience New Year's Eve 1999 in Sydney. I spent a year doing anything from removals, telemarketing and working for Greenpeace. I did hang out with some Neighbours cast. After chilling out in places like Singapore, Malaysia, Thailand, Burma and Laos, I moved to Korea to teach English.

It was there I started to get ill, especially on trips to Japan and China. In the end I was admitted to hospital and fell unconscious which is when my parents flew over as it was feared I would not last the weekend. I did. I got well enough to fly home and thought I would recover fast. But things did not really improve and soon I was on oxygen 24/7. When I was in Korea they damaged my trachea and I needed more than a dozen operations on it when I got home, which left me with damaged vocal chords.

I went on the transplant list for the best part of two years, with many false alarms, which meant long ambulance trips to Newcastle (many hours away).

Social networking was just becoming popular (this was pre-Facebook and Twitter) and I wrote a blog, http: wwwTransplantwait.blohspot.com which is still there but I seldom update it as I put most of my rants on Twitter/FB! I did regular .mp3 updates for the BBC, got my story published in women's and health magazines like Take A Break and sold stories to the media about blogging and what it was like waiting for a transplant. If it hadn't been for chatrooms (the craze in the 2003-5 era) I would have gone mad, it was good to converse with others. CF people are not encouraged to socialise face-to-face because of the risk of cross infection.

My life was on hold. We even had to make arrangements at my Dad's funeral in 2004, in case I got 'the call'. He died in the room next to me. I hadn't got the strength to resuscitate him. My Mum was my carer and I would be dead without her.

I got the call that mattered in October 2005, just a day before my birthday and woke up on my birthday with new lungs. I remember looking in the mirror and seeing movie-monster Predator looking back. I was let home in November (in the snow) and was again on BBC TV and an Inside Out documentary, reporters had been following my progress. There were a few hiccups but things went well. Soon after I got a new job as the press/PR officer for Halton Borough Council in Cheshire, and moved to Widnes.

I produce news stories, press releases, monitor the media, answer journalists' questions, update the new website, take pictures and write stuff for councillors to say. I do a lot of social media campaigns and have been mentioned in The Guardian for one I did encouraging people to use our libraries.

I joined The Volleyball Team for The Freeman and we had a weekend in Cambridge, where I met FHLTA members for the first time.

Then I got chronic rejection – I was in Prague on holiday, chatting to the singer, Pink, over hot wine and thought it was just an effect of all the smoke in the bars. There is no cure for this. You don't recover lost lung capacity.

I had just started being a guinea pig for an experiment at The Freeman, which I am always keen to do but my lung capacity was falling fast and they refused to put me on the drug, (I could have been on a placebo in the experiment). I had to go to Birmingham, where luckily my CF consultant was also a transplant expert. My lungs stabilised. It was depressing and I really thought this 'great new hope' of a new life had been a con.

My lung capacity is now between 20 and 25 per cent but it has been stable for almost nine years and I have seen people with higher capacities go downhill fast and die. It has been four years since I last had a day off sick.

Double gold in table tennis (singles & doubles), European Heart & Lung Championships, Vilnius, Lithuania June 2014.

I travel abroad frequently but avoid long flights. I have an active social life; go to gigs, the theatre and travel to see Aston Villa and Widnes Wild play ice hockey. I go to the gym four nights a week and can still play table tennis but have had to give up badminton, cricket, football and running (all which I enjoyed pre and post-transplant).

I can be walking on a treadmill and get rid of the stresses of the day as I have to put all my energy into breathing. It can get me down to see people who are so healthy after transplant, when I often find it a struggle. I first entered The Transplant Games in 2008 (Sheffield) and have been most years since, representing the UK in the

"The FHLTA is a great organisation of support and friendship and long may it continue to be so."

NHS Organ Donor Register:
0300 123 23 23
www.organdonation.nhs.uk

Europeans in Sweden, Holland and Lithuania. I am lucky enough to get medal(s) each time I compete.

I think my proudest moment post-transplant was carrying The Olympic Torch on the opening day of The Paralympic Games in London. I got to go from Lord's Cricket Ground, the home of cricket, towards Abbey Road. It got me more national coverage and again allowed me to promote organ donation. I am constantly in the local papers, on the radio and websites.

Olympic torch bearer for London 2012.

I didn't attend the recent racquets event – the table tennis was held in my home town – because I was at the FC Cup Final, but did loads of PR for it.

Halton Sport person of the Year award 2014.

Sports wise, I was named Halton Sport person of the Year 2014, after my golds in The European Games. I was also runner-up to Beth Tweddle for the regional title in 2012.

I always feel guilty I don't do more for The FHLTA, but I have done the odd sponsored event, including a weekend static bike cycle, when I passed the average age of death for a CF patient (37 years = 37 miles).

I recently did the transplant cycle event in Middlesbrough. I didn't complete the course in either of the two events I entered. But it was a personal goal achieved.

Transplant Sport cycling event, Middlesbrough June 2015.

Back in the Saddle

Michael Bradshaw

Born in 1950, I began cycling competitively from a young age, starting in 1966 as a junior. Soon afterwards I was the second fastest junior in the country in time trials, at the age of 17. In my later teens I decided to have a break from cycling, spending time doing typical daft teenage things, as you do.

At the ripe old age of 26 which would be 1976, the cycling bug bit and I once again began racing competitively, in 1977 posting the fastest 50 mile time of the year.

In 1978 I won National medals at all distances; 25, 50 and 100 mile time trials. I got married in 1980 and had a small break from cycling, taking up running for a while where I raced over numerous long distances including half marathons, 10k's etc...

I restarted my competitive cycling career in 1985. From 1985 to 1994, which was when I started to have problems with my heart, I won several more medals at National level. In 1988 in particular, I won the bronze medal in the 25 mile championships, gold in the 50 mile champs and was 4th in the 100 mile championships. All in all in my career I have won between 250-300 races up and down the country.

I have held multiple course records, some of which still stand to this day.

I was diagnosed with dilated cardiomyopathy in 1996 and had several pacemaker changes, the last three being Implantable Cardioverter Defibrillators (ICDs). I was unable to continue being a competitive cyclist. I became unemployable due to illness so my wife worked to support us. Over the years, I was becoming more and more unwell, until the end of 2014 whereby

I became seriously ill and was told I would need to stay in hospital until a heart became available for transplant. Subsequently I was in hospital for approximately 4 months. I eventually received a new heart on 5th December 2014. At the time of writing this story, it has been 6 months since my transplant and I have already thrown myself back into cycling. I have competed at The Transplant Sport Cycling Event in Middlesbrough on 20th June 2015, where I managed to win a silver medal.

Transplant has changed my life in that I am now training for my next challenge of The British Transplant Games in August 2015. I am riding approximately 200 training miles per week. It has enabled me to once again walk the dog and I'm able to resume life as it was before I was ill.

Whilst waiting for a transplant, my Transplant Co-ordinator, Lynne Holt, told me that The Freeman Heart and Lung Sports Team have a Cycling Team and from then on it has become my focus to get as fit as possible to ride in The Transplant Games. Having spent a lifetime of competitive cycling, it is great to be back in the saddle again.

"The medal I won at The Middlesbrough Cycling Event, I sent to my donor's family with a covering letter expressing my sincere gratitude for the gift of a second chance at life."

Seize the Day

Richard Lampert

I have had a busy and active time since I received a life-saving heart transplant at Newcastle's Freeman Hospital in 1987. Previously a healthy teenager, I had become critically ill with severe viral cardiomyopathy whilst taking my 'A' levels.

This caused me to suffer a major stroke and complete heart failure. I needed a heart transplant to survive and doctors warned me I would never walk again but following the transplant – and after plenty of intensive physiotherapy and a great deal of perseverance and hard work – I regained the ability to walk, along with the use of my left arm. Full recovery took a couple of years and by 1989 I was well enough to go to University before pursuing a career in IT.

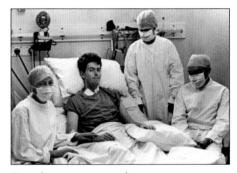

Two days post-transplant

Change, however, was just around the corner.

Following a spell of working as a computer developer, I was made redundant and decided on a complete change of direction. It was a good opportunity and the right time to try something new.

With the sea calling, and against doctors' advice, I studied to become a Water Sports Instructor at the UK Sailing Academy in Cowes, eventually qualifying not only as an RYA Senior Dinghy Instructor but also as a Powerboat Instructor and as an Assistant Windsurfing Instructor. Work at a number of outdoor education centres then followed, where I taught water sports to children and adults.

Sensing it was time to settle down, I eventually returned to the world of computing and since 1999 have worked in IT Training for the Open University in Milton Keynes where I live with my wife, Wendy. Whilst working fulltime I have continued sailing and cycling and have completed

a number of sponsored cycles for the British Heart Foundation. I also find time to pursue my other hobbies – photography and travelling.

In the 28 years since my transplant my health has been generally good.

I thank Chris McGregor, my surgeon and the team at The Freeman for giving me the transplant and giving me the full and rewarding life I now have.

Snowmobiling in Iceland

"I would like to urge everyone to sign the Organ Donor Register so that more critically ill people could get the opportunity that I was given for a new life."

A Year Today

Sharee McPhail

A year today when you got that call,
You were as brave as a soldier
And as strong as a wall
You went to theatre with your head held high,
With one last request.....
Please don't let me die
Brave, strong and stubborn
All typical of you....
You live today with lungs all shiny and new
Thanks to the skill of the medical team
And the selfless gift of the family of
Christine.

This poem was written by my sister, Samantha McPhail and her partner, Vicky Minshall for my 1ˢᵗ Transplant Anniversary.

I needed a transplant as I was at end stage Cystic Fibrosis.

Now, I am almost 4 years post-transplant and I've achieved way more than I could ever have dreamt of achieving including running a 10k and The BUPA Great North Run which I ran in 3hrs 45 minutes, exactly 13 months after my transplant (1 mile for every month!) I've had many bumps in the road post-transplant but I'd do it all again in a heartbeat.

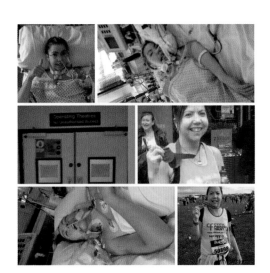

"I am eternally grateful to my donor and family."

NHS Organ Donor Register:
0300 123 23 23
www.organdonation.nhs.uk

My Father

Gary Leonard

Written by Sue Thompson, Gary's daughter

My Father is Gary Leonard and he received his heart transplant in March 1986. At the time I was a young child, I recall my Dad being in hospital and that he was having an important operation but at only 4 years old I was unable to grasp what exactly was happening and quite how important it was. Yet I always knew the treatment was necessary and that he was in the best possible place to get that. After all, as every young child knows, Doctors and Nurses are like Gods and can perform miracles. As an adult I still believe that! My memories are a little fragmentary and now that I'm in my 30's, I still have my child's eye view of the experience. I always think back to that time with fondness and love.

I lived with my Grandparents while my Dad was in hospital and was taken in frequently by them to visit him. I remember on one of these visits, while he was in intensive care after his successful operation, being told I needed to wear a gown. Having no concept of what this meant I stood still and waited to be robed like a princess; I found myself being put in a long white clinical gown that only came in adult sizes and it had to be rolled up at the sleeves so much that I imagine they probably resembled armbands at the swimming baths. A great deal of care had to be taken to avoid tripping on my new outfit, but it was worth it. I remember arriving at a large window and there was my Dad. I remember seeing his face light up when he saw me, he was genuinely pleased to see me and it showed. That feeling was entirely mutual. We brought a selection of my school work with us to show him, I can still feel my 4 year old pride swell as I held paintings and my first written words up at the window; my Dad put his thumbs up to show me he'd seen it and he loved it.

My most prominent memory of the time was when I celebrated my 5th birthday in the hospital. He was out of intensive care by this point and in a side room on a ward when we came in to visit and celebrate my birthday in the hospital. We had what seemed like the biggest cake I'd ever seen. It was pink with plastic ballet dancer figures on the top. Of course we shared it; the whole ward got a piece including patients, the doctors and nurses. I was even told about a man who was having surgery that day so we left some for him and the surgeon too. I can still remember the pile of loose change I ended up with as very kind gifts from those I'd shared my cake with. To a 5 year old it looked like the biggest pile of money in the world and if I'd thought about it at the time I'd probably have thought I was rich. My most treasured possession is a soft toy that was given to me on this day, a dog named Doughnut with long floppy ears and sad eyes. I still look at Doughnut and he reminds me of my wonderful and rather unique birthday, but he also reminds me of the gift of life that I now feel we were also celebrating on that day.

One of the funniest memories I have is after finding out at the time of my Dad's transplant that I was to become a big sister. I was asked on the way into the hospital one day if I would prefer a baby brother or sister. I wasn't sure which I wanted so I decided that the obvious option was to go for both. I was very disappointed to be told the baby had to be one or the other, not both at the same time.

My baby Sister was born in November 1986 and our family was complete. Since then we've made 1000's of wonderful memories, big and small, together with our Dad: day trips, holidays, the craft sessions we would have at the kitchen table, eating tea while watching our favourite TV programmes, sing-a-longs in the car, my Dad winning medals at the transplant games and me proudly showing them off in a presentation I gave at school, even the memory of my Dad trying to help my with my maths homework and myself not being able to understand it. They're all happy memories that we've been able to have together thanks to the precious gift my Dad received and the wonderful team at The Freeman Hospital who did the operation. For this I am eternally thankful.

Now our family is bigger; he now has Grandchildren and 2 Sons-in-Law and my Dad is still doing well, over 29 years later. We look forward to making many more happy memories together.

A Tribute Poem to My Dad, Gary Leonard and His Donor

Written by Stacey Asquith, Gary's daughter

Just a glimmer of hope as you lie in the bed, an operation to save your life,
Visitors wear robes and see you through glass, "I have some good news,"
said your wife.
A baby due for Christmas, a baby you might not have seen,
Had it not been for the lifesaving op,
for which you had doubts but were keen.
"If you live until Christmas the signs will be good," said the docs that gave
you the op,
You saw the baby (and Christmas) and knew this wasn't the time to stop.

You fought and you fought for your kindly given heart,
A new heart born of sorrow, but it gave *us* a fresh start.
Five years they then said and the outlook was good,
Skin now all pocked and scarred from giving blood.
A small price to pay as you watch your two girls grow,
We knew hospital visits would always be to and fro.
You watch us grow with a smile on your face,
Knowing that we could've all been in a very different place.
That 5 years went by and the docs then said TEN years,
But life was never without its worries and fears.
Thank God you were lucky as you reached the big ten,
"How long do you think?" you asked docs again.
They could not say how long you would live,
All dependant on how much your new heart could give.
You looked on with love as your daughters were now growing,
All great signs that your health was showing.

Dad with his two daughters;
Sue, on left and Stacey, on right.
November / December 1986.

You set yourself goals for a personal best, you wanted to see your girls wed,
Have children of their own, a life of their own, good grades and a really strong head.
Both of us graduated from Uni, I hope we both did you proud,
A tough time for you I guess, as these are our own lives we had found.
23 years on – your first grandchild is born, and I watched as you saw her at first,
Your eyes filled with tears, your heart with pride, I was sure you were going to burst.

You saw us rise, saw us fall and helped us to grow,
Your gifted heart was sure to overflow,
With the love that you had and the time that you gave,
Making sure that we were courageous and brave.
You walked me down the aisle, my Dad by my side,
To the love of my life, you walked me with pride.
This was a day I was convinced we wouldn't see,
Together, my Dad and me.

Dad with Granddaughter
Lily Jennifer, born Jan 2010.

Me and dad at my
wedding, Aug 2012.

A second grandchild on *your* birthday he was born,
26 years after your transplant, another of your
promises you had sworn.

My sister's turn to be wed, plans were made for you
to walk her too,
You became ill, but not with your heart, we made
sure she could come to you.

Dad with Grandson Quinlan
Leo. Born Feb 2013.

Sue's Wedding in hospital, Oct 2013.

We videoed the lot, thanks to modern day tech, and we drove to hospital to see you,
You remember so little of that day, and we had to talk about what we would do,
What if this was the end? What if this was your last? How would we cope without you?
But again you fought, like the hero you are and you came up trumps, you pulled through,
Now here we are and you're 29 years on and I ask you about your next goal,
You say you want to see us grow old, watch your grandkids as *they* take control.
As they grow up, get married, have kids, lead a full life of their own,
Then you'll look back on this wonderful life and think how *everyone's* grown.
And you'll think of a time, a long time ago, that there was a man who saved your life,
To him I want to say thank you and I'm sorry for his family's strife,
But if it wasn't for them and their lifesaving gift of a heart,
You wouldn't have met me and we would've have spent my entire life apart.
You've watched us live, watched us learn, watched us love,
From right here next to us, instead of from up above.

We love you, Dad!   x x

Domino Transplant

Andrew Jackson

I am happy to say that in November 2014 I celebrated my 25th Heart Transplant Anniversary.

My transplant at The Freeman Hospital was unique as it was a 'domino transplant'. You may wonder what a domino transplant is? Well, my new heart came from a live donor whom I had the privilege to meet. My donor was Penny Taylor from Horwich; sadly Penny had been born with Cystic Fibrosis and needed new lungs. Back in 1989 surgeons preferred to transplant heart and lungs together, therefore I was given the gift of Penny's heart, both transplants taking place the same evening.

I was fortunate to meet Penny, my donor, on several occasions.

Sadly, Penny died 2 years after her heart and lung transplant but my family and I will never, ever forget her. Thanks to the fantastic transplant team I continue to do well and live my life to the full.

I am looking forward to taking part in this year's transplant games, later this month.

Amelia's Story

Amelia loves making chocolates and started when she was a young girl making chocolate treats and sweets for her friends in The Brownies and Girl Guides.

When she was just 15 she had a heart transplant.

Tragically her brother died of a Hypertrophic Cardiomyopathy (hereditary heart disease) when Amelia was just 14. It was not known that any of Amelia's family suffered with this disease until her brother died and Amelia was diagnosed within 2 weeks of her brother dying. Amelia's heart was in such a bad condition she was told she needed a heart transplant to live.

Chocolate piping Amelia got the gift of life at 15. Undeterred and after recovering from the heart transplant, she left school, enrolled on a catering course and on completion, started a long apprenticeship as a Chocolatier at the locally famous Chocolate Factory in North Yorkshire. She went on to work in one of Scarborough's best known chocolate shops before embarking recently on her own business as a Master Chocolatier.

Today Amelia is 25 and to celebrate her 10 years of extra life she started a campaign to raise money for The British Heart Foundation, Live Life Then Give Life and the award winning Organ Donor Charity, where she is now an advocate.

Chocolate monkey, her aim was £10,000 – a thousand for each year of her life after her transplant. Today after a long campaign she has raised over £15,000. Amelia organised various events ranging from Winter Wonderland Ball, Coffee mornings and Chocolate Parties, at which her chocolates were sold.

Amelia also designed a Guide Challenge Badge for guiding units to take part in learning about Organ Donation and the heart, at the same time as having fun.

Amelia's story and those of other courageous, inspirational young people can be read on The Live Life Then Give Life site where it promotes to save and improve the lives of all those in need or receipt of organ and tissue transplants.

Waiting for a Second Chance of Life

Anne MacLennan

Every morning when I wake up I wonder if this could be the day that changes my life forever.

When the phone rings I hope this will be the call to say that they have found a lung or lungs for me.

Don't get me wrong, I am terrified of going through the operation and the recovery stages but I know it is the only realistic chance of anything which approaches having a normal life. Things that I have taken for granted in the past are impossible for me now so I am ready to take this leap of faith and go through the transplant procedure.

My heart is full of hope as I write this but it wasn't always like that, I can assure you.

Photo courtesy of Donald Fraser, Highland News.

About six years ago I was persuaded to go to the doctors by my support worker Annabel who works for The Homeless Trust in Inverness. She felt that I was suffering from depression but the doctor revealed to me that I actually had COPD and Emphysema. Only 32% of my lungs were working and this was going to get worse in the future. The news came as a bit of a shock to me but I had noticed that I was struggling to keep up with my friends when we were in town. I did not think much about the diagnosis until I was asked to go for further tests about two years later and my lung capacity had reduced to 24%. It is approximately 12% now. It was then we began talking about following the route to transplant.

My world came crashing down 18 months ago when I ended up in an induced medical coma in the Intensive Care Unit at Raigmore Hospital in Inverness. Apparently I had collapsed in one of the wards during one of my many emergency admittances to Raigmore. I was kept in for a month while doctors carried out numerous tests on me.

I was eventually allowed home but I now needed to be on oxygen 24/7 which was hard to adjust to. I was down to six stones in weight and would gasp for breath after walking more than three metres.

I suffer from severe anxiety and panic attacks and was admitted to Raigmore again on several occasions as the oxygen levels in my blood reached dangerously low levels.

In February 2015, I was invited down to The Freeman Hospital in Newcastle for a four day assessment. I was told that I needed to put on weight and get a bit fitter if I was to be put on the active list. My determination set in then and nothing was going to stop me reaching these goals. I was given three months to achieve the goals but managed to do it quicker than that and was seen sooner. I struggled with the six minute walk but finally cracked it and was put on the active list for double or single transplant. I felt like crying when I was told the news and cuddled the consultant.

While I was in Newcastle, Channel 5 started filming my story for a documentary programme called 'A Gift of Life' to be screened later in the year (2015).

I am obviously a bit scared but I am also excited about the new life I could have. Simple things like making meals, doing housework and even going for a bath are now a major undertaking for me. I can't go to see my grandchildren, drive my car or visit my friends, which makes me sad. My anxiety is still bad and my lack of breath causes anxiety and panic attacks. The unknown also makes me anxious. Will I die whilst on the active list? Will I make it to transplant? These are questions I continually ask myself.

I had been told about the Ex-Vivo Lung Perfusion technique and immediately signed the consent form for this to be used on me.

I am apprehensive about getting the call but above all I want to get it done so I can get on with my life. It is sad that someone has to die to give me the chance of life.

I would like to pay particular thanks to my best friend Mandy Barnett, of Forres, who has been with me every step of the way through my illness. She came with me to Newcastle on both occasions and will be coming with me if and when I get my transplant. She has been my rock. I would also like to thank the Homeless Trust and Raigmore Hospital in Inverness, who have been absolutely fantastic.

UPDATE: My first call on 02/07/2015

It was my 51st birthday on the 30th June 2015 and the whole day I was praying that this was going to be the day for my call which would have been the best gift ever in my life, but it didn't happen, the chances of it happening on my birthday was near to zero. No presents could replace what I really wanted for my birthday, my life back. But it was on my mind most of the day. I had a great day with my kids and grandkids visiting me and my friends.

On the 2nd of July my mobile went. No caller ID. It was Kirsty Wallace, my transplant coordinator on the other end and she said "Don't build your hopes up but there is a possible donor. " I got all excited to think this was a new beginning, about to start my new life. She said she was going to arrange everything: ambulance, flight etc, and then I phoned my friend Mandy who was working an hour away in council offices and she had to just jump in her car to get here before the flight. I phoned my kids and they travelled down by car.

Anne in wheelchair, with best friend, Mandy.

My carer was here at this point, my bag was already packed. I had to pack my Bi-Pap and medications, and then was all ready to go. I had such a mixture of excitement and fear; I thought I would be panicking but I didn't at all, I was so calm. I couldn't believe how calm I was. Then the ambulance turned up and they were taking me out of the door. Mandy just made it as I was getting put into the ambulance. This is really happening, I thought.

We got to a private plane. Wow! Just for me. I couldn't believe this was happening. A medic and 2 flight crew. I'm claustrophobic so for the first 5 minutes I felt a bit anxious, but the medic and Mandy kept my mind occupied. An hour later we arrived in Newcastle where an ambulance with flashing blue lights rushed me through Newcastle to The Freeman, where I was taken to the ward and given a bed. From this point, it was a waiting game, as Kirsty explained that the lungs had not been checked yet. There was also a delay as another team were busy assessing other organs for transplant. Kirsty had said we should know around 9pm. As midnight approached I was still waiting, but I already had a feeling it was a no go and possibly a dry run, so when Kirsty came round after midnight and said the lungs were very diseased and that they want the best for me, I was relieved to know they were thinking of me and they were not going to just transplant any badly damaged lungs. They want me to live the maximum number of years I can after transplant. I was a bit disappointed but I thought it was not my time and not meant to be and maybe second time lucky. When I got home the following day I was exhausted for a few days as the journey took a lot out of me. However, I'm so glad I did it and know it's hopefully not going to be long till I get the 'Gift of Life'. I can't wait for my next call and hope it's second time lucky. I had so many people around the globe praying for me.

I appreciate how well organised my travel was and the money the NHS has spent on me, trying to save my life. I will never be able to thank Kirsty Wallace and the Staff at The Freeman Hospital enough. Neither so the Staff and Specialist Dr Patterson at Raigmore Hospital and all of the ward staff. I was treated like a queen and I appreciate all of you.

> **"I do hope one day I will get another call and hope it's going to be sooner than later. I will wait patiently for the next call. Thank you."**

For All Donor Families

Written on behalf of Jim Moore aka China

By good friend Freda Williamson

I really want to thank you
For The gracious gift you gave
I really want to thank you
For your decision was very brave
I really want to thank you
As you grieved throughout the pain
I really want to thank you
A normal life that I'd gain
I really want to thank you
Thank you is all I can say
I really want to thank you
And thank you every day!!!

NHS Organ Donor Register:
0300 123 23 23
www.organdonation.nhs.uk

In Memory of My Mum

Written by Beth Hodgson, in Memory of her Mum Linzi Featherston

´... Cystic fibrosis is the most common genetic disease in the UK, with every 1 in 20,000 of the population a carrier of the two recessive alleles that cause disease. It primarily affects the respiratory and digestive tract...´

How can printed letters, so uniform and neat, ever do justice to the true nature of a disease? Every sentence is filled with a million words that once upon a time meant nothing and yet, they are lacking somehow, devoid of the human emotion that makes the disease so real. It often seems the case. For all the pictures of festering wounds, diagrams of drugs and biochemistry and perfect anatomical representations, the patient´s story is buried in it somewhere. Told in hesitant, fumbling words or with an anxious rush of feeling, you can find it there, with a human face and flesh and blood and a family. Just the same as you and I but somehow, even those words aren´t enough. Sure they can conjure empathy and sympathy and all those other things we get told we should feel when the patient spills out their fears but even that is not enough. Because until it is you sat in that chair, facing the doctor or sat beside a hospital bed, clinging to a hand, how can you possibly know how it feels or what it does to a person?

And these very words before me, talking about Pseudomonas and sinuses and antibiotics and all the things that go along with it reduce the patient to nothing more than a disease. They don´t stop to consider how that person might have to drive 50 feet because they struggle to walk, or how climbing out of a bath leaves them breathless, terrified. They don´t discuss how that person is probably struggling with the knowledge of a shortened life-span or the difficulty they face in trying to buy travel-insurance.

But I know. I have seen it, first-hand. I was there alongside them in the car when we had to drive around the corner to see my Grandparents, I was there when they had to sit and calm their breathing after a bath. I was there when we had to have extra oxygen on the plane, when the bottles invaded our home. I was there.

Yet the text before me almost breaks them down into nothing more than their illness. It defines that patient, that person, by one single aspect of their whole entire life. It says ´Look, here is a person. They have flesh and blood and a beating human heart. They grew up just like you, they have loved and hated and suffered and been so gloriously happy they could fly, just like you. But never mind all that, forget for a moment and look past it all. Here is their illness. Focus on that. Because that is what they are.´ But an illness does not define an individual.

And when I think about my mum, I do not think of her as a ´CF -er´. I was only eight years old when she had her double lung transplant, you see, almost seventeen when she died. But when I think of her, I think of her hands as she cut my hair, having just completed a course in hair and beauty, I think of her smile in Florida whilst we swam with dolphins, her coming back from the gym, so bright and full of life.

A double lung transplant gave my mum another eight years of life, another eight years with me. It wasn´t easy at the time. The transplant itself took twice as long as normal, the recovery long and painful with more than one setback. But she pulled through in the end and came home to me. And it wasn´t a cure, of course it wasn´t, but she could get married, take longer walks on the beach, make plans for a future.

Of course, she passed away eight years later. But then all things must end and as a famous singer once said, only the good die young. So perhaps it isn´t the miracle story that transplantation normally heralds, perhaps it doesn´t have a happy ending. But those eight years have meant the world to me.

It meant I got to grow up with a mum.

Beth and her Mum, Linzi

We got to have adventures and take photos and have massive, blistering arguments that all teenagers must have, we got to go clothes shopping and play dominoes and watch stupid daytime television. And those are the memories that come to me now, reading the stark paragraph of clinical terms. And those are the memories that will stay with me.

And so when I see you on the ward in three years times, stethoscope in hand and newly acquired 'Dr' in my name, I will smile and ask you a million questions and listen attentively to every answer you give me not because I must, but because I want to. Because I know that you are somebody else´s mum, somebody else´s daughter and above all else, that you too have a beating human heart.

NHS Organ Donor Register:
0300 123 23 23
www.organdonation.nhs.uk

From Transplant to New Beginnings

Bronwyn Jones

Twelfth of July 2009. A day that is etched in my memory as that is the day I was diagnosed with dilated cardiomyopathy (a form of heart failure).

My life changed forever. Suddenly I was disabled, I felt singled out by illness and it felt as if everyone looked at me differently. I had had some symptoms for a while but really didn't know what they were. I had been feeling breathless, tired, faint and dizzy, however, these symptoms were not constant, they came and went and they were easy to explain away by other things.

Once I was diagnosed, the biggest symptoms became depression and anxiety. My life was consumed by my illness. I made the fatal mistake of looking up my illness on the internet and the outlook was not good. From that day on I lived with the constant fear of dying.

Over the course of the following year my illness progressed until finally, 11 months after diagnosis, my heart failed completely and I was admitted to Kings Mill Hospital. After examination by consultant cardiologist Dr. J Rowley, it soon became clear that my only chance was to receive a new heart and I was transferred by ambulance, under blue light, all the way to The Freeman Hospital in Newcastle-upon-Tyne. On arrival I was immediately admitted to intensive care and I underwent a battery of tests to ascertain my suitability for transplant.

My husband and other members of my family arrived at the hospital the next day and soon the doctors were sitting us all down and explaining to us what would happen next. Once my suitability to receive a heart had been confirmed I went on the transplant list and was told I was number 1 on the list as my need was so great.

By this time, I was extremely ill and in addition to my heart having failed, my liver had failed and also my kidneys. Consequently, I was put on kidney dialysis to help clear the toxins in my blood. My memory of this time is very intermittent as I was drifting in and out of consciousness. I remember the doctors and nurses constantly monitoring me and it was during this period that my heart stopped twice and I needed to be resuscitated.

I was looked after by a whole team of specialists, including a Professor of Cardiothoracic Surgery who eventually did my operation. I also had one to one nursing in intensive care so I really did have the best care possible.

Within 6 days of going on the transplant list, a new heart became available. The heart was a good match and was the right size for my body.

As a patient you are told that an organ has become available but then have a long wait until you know whether the operation will definitely be going ahead. This is because a team of doctors have to do extensive tests on the organ to make sure that it is suitable for transplant to optimise the patient's chances of a good recovery and a long life after transplant.

My operation went ahead at 4am in the morning and only lasted about 4 hours. I was one of the lucky ones. I had a text book recovery and was out of intensive care within 4 days.

Day by day I got a bit better and a bit better and was soon eating and up and about. The first time my husband took me out for a walk in the wheelchair was a day I will never forget. I thought I was in heaven. Life suddenly never felt so good. I had a great big smile on my face just because I was out in the fresh air. The feel of the warm sunshine on my face

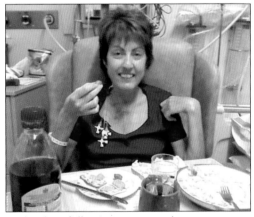

In the days following my transplant.

and the warm September breeze felt wonderful. (I had been stuck inside hospital for about 6 weeks all in all).

Once home from hospital, life followed a pattern of regular hospital visits for many, many months. This was to monitor my progress and to check for possible rejection.

Within 6 months, I was back at work and life began to resemble some semblance of normality. Since then, I have gone from strength to strength and life feels really good. I have suffered no rejection and very few infections.

I constantly think about my donor. I have made contact, through the hospital, with his family and now know a little about him and his life.

I thank God every day for the wonderful gift of life that my donor gave me. Without him and his family I would not be here today. Also my husband would be a widower and my children would have no mum.

I try each day to live life to the full and enjoy every moment. I don't 'sweat the small stuff' and just get on with things.

My clinical outlook is good. Although the hospital gives you statistics on life expectancy after transplant, I don't take any notice of them. There are plenty of patients at the transplant clinic who are still doing really well after 20 years plus and I am determined I am going to be one of them.

"I would urge anyone who has ever hesitated about signing the organ register to think again. I never thought I would need a new organ, most people don't. However, you have to ask yourself if you or a loved one needed a new organ, would you accept one? If the answer is yes, then you really have to sign up to the register and agree to donate yourself."

NHS Organ Donor Register:
0300 123 23 23
www.organdonation.nhs.uk

Our Hero

Derek Airey (written by his wife, Patricia Airey)

Me and my husband Derek.

My husband Derek served in The Royal Air Force for over twenty five years. After retiring he lead a very busy and active life and to both himself and others seemed to be a very healthy man.

One morning I received a phone call from Newcastle General Hospital informing me Derek had suffered a massive heart attack.

After Derek had undergone investigation from the doctors, I was informed that for my husband to survive he would require a heart transplant, he was instantly placed on the organ waiting list.

The next eighteen months was mainly spent in hospital and before my very own eyes my husband's health was fast deteriorating.

On holiday in Las Vegas.

The night we received the phone call he was so calm and positive about what was about to happen. Derek was so determined that the operation was something he had to get through in order to get on with his life both as a husband and as a granddad.

The last 22 years have not come without complications, but I know first-hand how grateful Derek is to his donor family for giving him the chance to watch his grandchildren grow from babies to the young women they are now.

Derek & family attending the graduation ceremony of granddaughter Rachel.

Derek is back to living a very busy and active life, regularly swimming and representing his country at The World Transplant Games.

Derek devotes so much time to being The FHLTA Chairman and is very involved in not only promoting organ donation but supporting other transplant patients with any problems they come across.

Derek at the British Transplant Games.

My family and I are forever grateful for everything that both Freeman Hospital and the FHLTA have done for Derek over the years.

2012 – A Good Year

Doreen Collingwood

I had struggled through most of my life with chest problems. When I was just 6 months old doctors thought I may have had whooping cough. I was the kid that always caught a cold and as I got older I struggled more and more, I found any kind of sport incredibly difficult despite my slender frame. I was diagnosed with asthma at around 16 years old.

As the years passed, things didn't get any easier and chest infection followed chest infection. After much dilemma, stays in hospital, pneumonia and even a collapsed lung, I was finally given the most likely cause and therefore the most probable diagnosis was due to Cystic Fibrosis. At this point, my lungs were scarred and damaged beyond repair and a double lung transplant, the only option. I was placed on the active list in March 2011.

Just weeks before my transplant I was lucky enough to see The Olympic Flame being carried through my village, however, I had a dilemma because on the same day I had been invited to a family christening. I wanted to do both but knew it would be a struggle, planning to do anything pre transplant was a struggle. Most of the time you feel so exhausted and all the mundane tasks that most people do without thinking like getting showered, getting dressed and to be honest just getting out of bed on a morning, was a struggle. So when you are gasping for every breath, these everyday tasks need planning and time, lots and lots of time.

For me, wanting to see The Olympic Flame and going to a family gathering in one day, well this was going to be a mammoth task but I was going to do both, regardless. So oxygen in hand I walked the few steps from my house to the top of the street where I live, even on a good day it took all my effort to make it from my front door to the car! There was quite a crowd of people gathered, well it's not everyday something like this happens here. We all stood clapping and cheering whilst the parade of vehicles passed, I was even high fived by a police motorcyclist, almost took my hand off; my wrists were so weak by this point due to severe arthritis in my joints which was most likely a consequence of the inflammation in my lungs. Finally the Olympic Torchbearer appeared with the 2012 flame in hand, to a massive cheer and applause. I was late for the Christening, we

Pre-transplant, June 2012.

arrived just as the service had finished but it was worth it. As for me, there was something symbolic about seeing that flame on that day.

Just a few weeks later I was lying in a hospital bed watching the opening ceremony of the 2012 London Olympic Games. I was in recovery following a life-saving double lung transplant that would change my life. I spent just 2 weeks in hospital before I was discharged and finally I was able to do those little things that everyone does without thinking such as brush my teeth, wash my hair and take a shower. Little steps at first but you have to learn to walk before you can run.

Three years on and I have since participated in my very own Olympic Games; at the 2015 Newcastle / Gateshead British Transplant Games, something I would never have thought possible before my transplant. I took part in a number of events and did not expect to win any medals so was overwhelmed to win a Gold medal in 10 pin bowling and a Bronze medal in the 3km walk, as well as receiving a medal for completing the 3km Donor walk / run. This has been my first major sporting event as a member of The Freeman Heart & Lung Transplant Team and since joining I have been lucky enough to meet so many lovely and inspiring people.

Me with Alan Shearer at the British Transplant Games Donor Run Launch, July 2015

To be honest we inspire each other. Our stories are all different but we share something very special, we have all been fortunate enough to be able to live the lives we could only have dreamed of pre transplant.

"Thanks to our donors and their families – always in our thoughts."

National Memorial for Organ & Tissue Donors, Scotland Royal Botanic Garden Edinburgh

Gill Hollis

One of the recommendations of the Organ Donation Taskforce in 2008 was that *"appropriate ways should be developed to recognise individual donors"*. In Scotland, we already had a memorial, a wooden love-seat in Glasgow's Kelvingrove Gallery, to which a silver leaf has been added for every deceased organ donor. It was established in 2000, but by 2012 little space remained on it. However, in order to create a new memorial, we had two basic requirements – obtaining funding and a suitable site. We were extremely lucky, in that the Scottish Government agreed to provide funding and the Royal Botanic Garden Edinburgh (RBGE) agreed to provide a tranquil, secure and beautiful location.

A steering group was set up to oversee the project. This was to be a memorial primarily to remember donors, so donor families were obviously represented. But reflecting the fact that donation and transplantation is a huge team effort, all parts of the transplant community were represented. I was privileged to represent transplant recipients. Finally, acknowledging that, though enthusiastic, we were not perhaps the most creative and arty group of people, we were joined by representatives from Creative Scotland, the Edinburgh Sculpture Workshop and the RBGE. Their practical help and guidance was invaluable!

In late 2012, we distributed a brief for the project and invited submissions. The response was fabulous, but in the end we chose the artist and poet Alec Finlay, not only because we liked his recent work and his initial ideas for our project, but particularly because he showed empathy and a genuine interest in what we were trying to achieve, and why.

Certainly, in the following months, Alec spent considerable time meeting individuals to help him understand the complex and sensitive relationships between all of us whose lives have been touched by organ or tissue donation. That understanding and sensitivity comes through in what he and his team of collaborators have created. The memorial features a dry-stane 'taigh' (Gaelic for 'house') with a turf-roof which seals in a set of river stones. Buried under the foundations is a memorial book containing the first names of every organ and tissue donor in Scotland between 2006 and late 2013. The surrounding 'wilding garden' is also home to a 'font' containing pebbles collected from beaches around Scotland, and two beautiful circle poems carved into stone:

"...nothing that ends in a gift ends in nothing..."
and
"...the light of those taken from the light..."

The memorial was officially opened in September 2014 and in this peaceful little glade we now have an exceptionally special place to celebrate some exceptionally special people. It's impossible to thank my donor enough for the gift that they gave me but I love having a place that recognises and remembers them. I'd encourage everyone to visit the memorial; it is close to and signposted from the East Gate of the Royal Botanic Garden Edinburgh.

Donor Memorial:
Credit to Taigh, Alec Finlay; Photograph by Hannah Devereux.

Four page leaflet featuring The Memorial for Organ and Tissue Donors at The Royal Botanical Garden, Edinburgh. Leaflet courtesy of The Scottish Government.

Life – The Most Amazing Gift of All

Susan Burton (Trustee for Donor Family Network)

The Donor Family Network's Gift of Life Memorial is sited at the National Arboretum at Alrewas, Staffordshire.

The charity's vision for a national memorial to honour those donors and their families who made the gift of life possible came to fruition following a number of years of fund-raising, planning and designing.

The final design, developed by Julia Hennessey-Priest, is based on The Donor Family Network's logo and features a butterfly and a forget-me-not. The butterfly, a symbol of hope and new life, is constructed from cast bronze with inlaid mosaic tiles, resting on a forget-me-not as no donor will ever be forgotten. The memorial, which is a metre in diameter, stands on a plinth of Welsh slate.

The memorial pays tribute to organ and tissue donors, transplant recipients, those who sadly died whilst waiting for a transplant and those whose wishes could not be fulfilled.

The memorial encompasses three themes:
- Reflection – A place of reflection and contemplation for all those whose lives have been touched by organ and tissue donation and transplantation.
- Recognition – A place to recognise all those who donated for the benefit of others.
- Remembrance – A place where all donors and those who died whilst waiting for a transplant will be remembered with love.

The Donor Family Network hopes that those families who visit the memorial will gain some peace and comfort and that it will encourage other visitors to the Arboretum to consider organ and tissue donation.

Donor Family Network are arranging for an official opening ceremony in Spring 2016 and hope that many of those whose lives have been affected by organ and tissue donation will be able to attend.

The Gift of Life Memorial

NHS Organ Donor Register:
0300 123 23 23
www.organdonation.nhs.uk

Never Lose Hope

Giles McVicar

I had been very well and active for all my life up until October 1989, when aged 17, I suddenly started to feel breathless whilst playing sport at school. My GP was unsure what the diagnosis was and he eventually admitted me to hospital, where they quickly discovered that I had Cardiomyopathy.

I received 6 weeks of treatment and strict bed rest but my condition was deteriorating all the time and at the very start of Jan 1990, I was placed on the emergency list for a heart transplant, at Killingbeck Hospital, Leeds. From just after Christmas time I remember nothing as I was too ill, and from then it was estimated that I had about 2 weeks to live. I was still hanging on, when on Jan 14th, a heart became available and I received the heart of a gentleman in his 60's.

My recovery was very slow and complicated and my body weight had halved to around 6 1/2 stone but after 2 weeks in intensive care and a further 6 weeks on the ward I was able to go home.

My focus now was to get back to a totally normal life and 6 months later I returned to school to complete my A Levels. I was able to start playing golf again and a friendly game of football but rugby was not possible. I felt as well I had done before my illness although I couldn't attain the same fitness levels or body strength. Then, in 1992, I was fortunate to start a career in banking at RBS.

After 2 months of work, I was diagnosed with Lymphoma. This was successfully treated with Chemotherapy and Radiotherapy.

I was then able to live a fully active and 'normal' life again until I collapsed unconscious whilst playing football in 1997. My arteries had narrowed and so at this time I was referred to the fantastic team at The Freeman Hospital, where I was placed on the transplant list again, in mid-1997, for another heart.

I was able to keep working right the way up until I received my second heart transplant in Jan 1999, aged 26. The operation went very smoothly and my recovery was much quicker this time as I was still reasonably well. According to Mr Dark, the heart I received was 'very good' and a perfect match. The donor was a male of similar age to me whose life had unfortunately been taken in a motorbike accident.

Having gained my strength back, I returned to work mid-1999 and became engaged to Susan later that year. I was soon able to resume playing golf and other sports again. However, in May 2000, the Lymphoma relapsed and I received further Chemotherapy, which was successful in sending it back into remission.

In 2001, Susan and I married and then in Feb 2003, our first son Harry was born.

In mid-2004, the Lymphoma returned again and I received further Chemotherapy. The immunosuppressants were unfortunately 'encouraging' the cancer. Then, in 2005, we were fortunate to have our second son, Robert.

I had further Lymphoma relapses in 2006, 2007, 2008 and 2009 which were treated with Radiotherapy, Chemotherapy, a change in immunosuppressants and a chest operation. The operation led to me developing pneumonia, which was successfully treated and then a further slight relapse of Lymphoma was diagnosed, but not treated. My employers, (still RBS), were fantastic and I managed to work as much as I could through these difficult years.

By Jan 2011, I needed further treatment for the Lymphoma and I started more Chemotherapy. This was stopped in July that year and I then had a further episode of Pneumonia followed by Septicaemia.

By Aug 2012, my Kidneys had decided they'd had enough and I was told I'd need a kidney transplant, only for them then to quickly recover sufficiently enough for me to avoid dialysis or a possible transplant.

The momentum of illness had become too great and so the RBS kindly granted me early retirement from my Senior Business Manager role, in Dec 2012.

From that point on I have remained in very good health, the Lymphoma hasn't reappeared and my kidneys are stable. I've been very active playing sport, dog walking, doing voluntary work and looking after my family.

Amazingly, throughout my story I have hardly had to mention my heart (or hearts)!

I am now 43 and without my 'first' heart I would have died aged 17.

Then, without my 'second' heart I would have died aged 26, having not been able to marry or bring my two wonderful boys into the world.

With my 2 sons

The immensely brave decisions of the donors' families, the incredible skill of all the medical staff who have cared for me and latterly, a strengthening faith have brought me to the here and now!

"To agree to donate an organ must be an incredibly hard decision for a lot of people but it's the biggest gift you can ever give anyone. You're giving someone life when they face death. I am extremely thankful."

NHS Organ Donor Register:
0300 123 23 23
www.organdonation.nhs.uk

My Transplant Story

Susan Wrightson

My transplant story really begins almost 26 years ago when I had a stroke. I was 23 at the time. It's very frightening to wake up and be told you have had a stroke at such a relatively young age. It was caused because my already bad heart was failing faster than thought by anybody.

I had been born with severe heart conditions including transposition of the major vessels and fairly useless valves between both atria and ventricles (top and bottom chambers of the heart). The blood is supposed to stay in the ventricles once it has been pumped there by the atria but it flowed back into the atria causing very poor circulation and me to be blue all the time. Together with this, my heart and everything else inside me was on the wrong side of my body. It's not a problem medically, as long as it all works ok.

Following being discharged after the stroke, I visited the Cardiologist at Alder Hey Children's Hospital to let the doctor see me after for discussion as to what was to be done to prevent further strokes. At that visit he told me I would need a heart transplant as I had already had three very major operations done to my heart and it was unlikely to be made any better by further intervention to it. My original reaction was to say "No, I'm not that ill, you can keep me going on more tablets." That was in September 1989.

In December I was dismissed from my job as they said I was taking too much time off for medical appointments. That Christmas, I decided, together with my parents, to agree to the transplant. We went back to Alder Hey in the New Year and told the doctor there of our decision. I went through the tests needed to be accepted for transplantation and in November 1990 I was accepted and put onto the active list. I was issued with a bleep and told to ring Freeman Hospital, Newcastle upon Tyne if I got a bleep as it was possible for it to pick up stray bleeps. It did this a few times and at all hours of the day and night.

 It went off in October 1991, in late afternoon. Dad drove me up to Freeman Hospital, a journey of approximately three hours from our home. I was fully prepared for the surgery, I had blood samples taken, dressed for theatre and had the dose of Ciclosporin (an anti-rejection drug), prior to surgery. Then Mr Dark walked into the room I was in on Ward 27A and told us that the transplant would not be going ahead as the donor heart had been too badly damaged in the accident.

That news is the worse news I have ever received in my life and I can fully empathise with patients when they have to be told their operation is not going ahead for whatever reason.

On 2nd January 1992 (23 years ago) I got a bleep again and this time the operation went ahead. I was taken to theatre about 8pm and transferred to ICU at about 2am on the 3rd January. My parents saw me at that time and my Mum remembers seeing me pink for the first time in my life. I recovered quickly and started to fight the ventilator at 8am and was taken off it at 9am. I don't remember very much really as I was probably still very dozy from the anaesthetic. I was transferred to Ward 27A at 2pm on 3rd January approximately 12 hours after my operation finished.

I recovered well but I got a cold when I was about three weeks post operation. At first the doctors thought my lungs were collapsing so did a bronchoscopy on me. I don't remember this as I was given something

to make me very drowsy for the procedure. I also had a series of blood samples taken from me and had a chest x-ray. The day after the doctors got confirmation that the illness I was suffering was nothing more than a cold. I also had rejection while I was in the hospital. I recovered from this successfully too.

Since leaving hospital, I have been fortunate enough to have had quite good health, certainly as far as the transplant. I had a

Sue winning silver in archery, Bolton 2014.

fairly serious rejection when I was four years post op. This lasted for six months with no improvement, then suddenly it improved. My visits went from once a fortnight to less frequently, quite quickly, as I got more stable. I still have to go for visits every three months.

Since my transplant I have met and married my husband, qualified as a tutor and later as a nurse.

I have competed in The British Transplant Games since 1999 and have taken up archery as a result of this. I am the current gold medallist in my category (2015). I have also competed in The European Heart and Lung Transplant Games and as a result have visited many countries including Norway, Austria and Lithuania to name a few. As a result of my transplant I have met people from many countries and all over the UK. I continue to keep in contact with many of them by way of Facebook.

Above: Me and my old dog, Jim, taking part in agility training, one of my keen interests.

Heart to Heart

Stephen and Rachael (written by Mary Moffat)

My name is Mary. I work as a midwife at Wishaw General Hospital, Motherwell and want to encourage people to join the Organ Donor Register in a bid to save more lives like my children's, who both had heart transplants at The Freeman Hospital.

Stephen and Rachael at The British Transplant Games, August 2015.

Over 40 per cent of Scots have already made their wishes known by joining the NHS Organ Donor Register, but it's vital you tell your family to ensure your wishes are carried out should anything happen to you.

In the year that my daughter Rachael started school, she was really tired all the time. I would come home from work every day and find her sleeping. My other kids would want to get up at the weekend and do stuff, but she would just want to sleep. She would also fall asleep in really odd places. I thought that there was something wrong and discussed my concerns with my mother-in-law.

My husband had a blocked aorta when he was young and she saw the same symptoms in Rachael as she had seen in my husband. I took Rachael to the paediatrician at Wishaw Health Centre, who referred her to Yorkhill Children's Hospital.

At the time Rachael was referred to Yorkhill, my husband called me at work to say that my son Stephen had collapsed. He was ten years old at the time. There was no lead up to it. He was very active and had wanted to be a professional footballer.

When Stephen collapsed for a second time, he was also referred to Yorkhill. After their tests, we went back to the clinic to see the consultant. I knew something was really wrong and I tried everything to keep my mind off the news that I was going to get. The consultant told us that both children had a condition called Restrictive Cardiomyopathy.

When you are told something like that, you can't take it in. I was really upset and you try to think that it must be someone else's children that they are talking about. I knew of people who had Restrictive Cardiomyopathy and hadn't survived.

Both Stephen and Rachael looked really well at the time they were diagnosed. I tried to persuade myself that the specialists had made a mistake and that my children were OK. Both I and my husband were also given tests, which resulted in him also being diagnosed with the condition.

Both children were quickly added to the waiting list for a donor heart.

Two weeks after joining the register, Stephen was offered a transplant. Due to his age, he had a better chance of finding an organ than a younger child would have had. Eight months later, Rachael received hers.

They both received their transplants within a year of being diagnosed, which is extremely quick. They have kept really well since.

I Met a Friend Today

John Docherty

I met a friend today for the first time
It was in a strange place and we were both a long way from home
We travelled a different route and walked a different path
But we ended up together in the same time and the same space

This place we meet very few get to see and very few get to be
It seems it's reserved only for you and only for me
But others will join us very soon
Under the stars and under the moon

The stage is set and the actors are there
I think it's more than we both can bear

So In the theatre are the great and the good
Ready to perform as only they could
We watch from a distance to see what's going on
But nothing prepared us for being reborn
We took a break and walked for a while
Just to see each other's style

As we walked and talked in each other's head
I never thought one of us was dead
We had some great times and told each other stories
About our lives and all their glories our families and friends
And those still to meet as we walked along the very same street

Now my friend and I have our own point of view
About how we ended up here and what we've to do
Our roles are different but then just the same
It all depends what you see in your brain

Now back in the theatre it's just you and me
All set for whatever will be
We're happy to do this and the roles have been set
As the surgeon stands over and opens my chest
We leave it to him who thinks he knows best

NHS Organ Donor Register:
0300 123 23 23
www.organdonation.nhs.uk

Now on the table with my chest open wide
I see my friend with a gift of life
I looked in his eyes and see all before me
A true friend in all his glory

We said our goodbye but it's not the end
It's only the beginning as we are back with the living

13/10/2012 I met a friend today
We didn't have that long together but will be part of each other's life forever
I will carry with me the love, grace and kindness that he must have had, with pride
In everything I do, in everything I see, and every breathe I take, I will not do alone
Because I met a friend today

Lung transplant patient
John

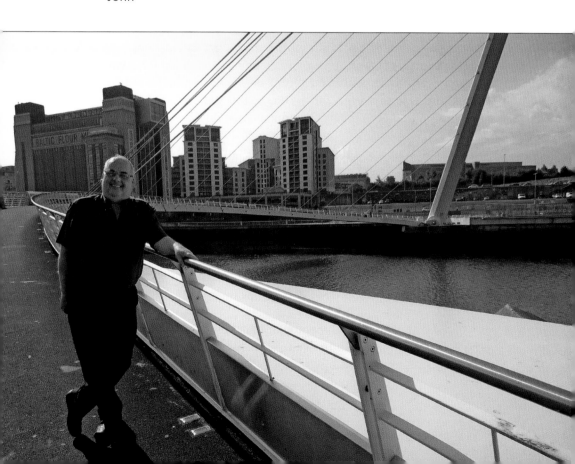

Florida, Here I Come!

Libby Nash

I was born with Cystic Fibrosis and diagnosed at the age of 3yrs in 1987. CF is a genetic condition that affects the lungs and digestive system which then made me vulnerable to repeated lung infections.

This entailed a lot of medication, hospital visits and physiotherapy. I was admitted to hospital every 3 months for IV treatment due to the chest infections which also affected my weight so at the age of 5yrs I started doing NG tube feeding to help build up my weight.

As the years went on my lung function was deteriorating and chest infections were more frequent which meant I had to be put onto oxygen during the night at the age of 14yrs.

Growing up with CF affected every aspect of my life; I missed a lot of school and also had to do some of my GCSE papers in hospital and at home as I was too unwell to attend school.

Physically I wasn't able to do all the things my friends were doing like playing sports, going shopping and clubbing. Just going for a walk, even walking around the house and getting dressed was a battle as I got so out of breath. I was on oxygen 24hrs a day by this stage. All I wanted was to be normal and to do the things everyone else could do.

In 2006 it was suggested to me that I might need to think about transplantation as my lung function was at 25% and was dropping after every chest infection.

I went to The Freeman Hospital in Newcastle in August 2006 for my assessment and to discuss all the pros and cons about going ahead with the double lung transplant. I decided that this was the best option for me to try and have a better life as there is no cure for CF. I was put on the active transplant list shortly after.

I had my first call within 6 months of being on the list but unfortunately the lungs were not a good match. Over the following 2 years I received another 3 calls for a possible transplant but again they were not a match to me due to different reasons. In total I waited 6 years and received 7 possible transplant calls.

The wait for the transplant was long; when the phone rang you would always wonder if this could be the call, especially if they had an English accent or it was late at night. As the years went on all I could think of was if this was ever going to happen for me or would I just be adding to the number of people who die waiting for a transplant. We found ourselves living day to day and making sure I was always contactable as you just never know when that call will come, we even had to take our pre-packed bags with us if we travelled more than an hour from home as you had to get to the closest airport, wherever you were.

While waiting on the list, you have your good days and bad. On the good days you would sometimes try to forget about being on the list and just carry on with things but on the bad days you just wanted the call to come through. Then guilt would set in because I knew someone would have lost their life in order for me to live but I just took each day as it came and tried to stay positive.

During my wait for the transplant I married James in 2008. That was the most nervous day and the only one I hoped the call did not come. We were unable to go on honeymoon as I didn't want to come off the transplant list. I wanted to go to Florida and be able to enjoy walking around the parks without getting tired or needing oxygen.

In June 2012, things took a turn for the worse, I became seriously ill as I woke up one day and just didn't feel myself so James rushed me up to Belfast City Hospital. While in the car my head fell forward and I had stopped breathing for a few seconds which seemed forever to him, but thankfully I came round.

When I got to the hospital the CF team began to run all different tests urgently to find out what the problem was and my lung function had dropped below 14%. A few hours later I was told I had end stage lung failure and the CO_2 levels in my body were extremely high as my lungs were not exchanging gases and so I was rushed into ICU. The ICU and CF team tried several different options like the bi Pap machine but nothing worked.

They came and told us that there was not much more they could do and I thought to myself, this is the end, but a few hours later I was given a

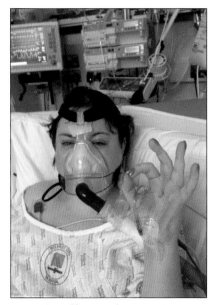

In ICU in Belfast on the Novo Lung, waiting for my transplant and trying to keep a smile on my face but knowing that it might never happen (I had even planned my own funeral, just in case).

lifeline. Newcastle doctors decided to put me onto a new machine called the Nova Lung as a bridge to transplantation.

The best way for me to describe the Nova Lung is, it is like a dialysis machine. It pumped blood out, oxygenated it and then pumped it back into me. This came with its own complications. The people who designed the Novo Lung, from Germany, had to be brought over and the rep for the machine, Donal, who was in Dublin, had to come up as well as this machine had never been used in The Belfast City Hospital.

Once everyone was there, they tried to put a line into my femoral artery (in my groin area) as they couldn't put it into my neck be-cause they required that vein for the transplant if it came through. They couldn't put me to sleep as every time I relaxed to go asleep, I would stop breathing. They connected me to the machine but found out that the line they used was not big enough for the flow of blood so they had to call a specialist vascular surgeon to put in a bigger line as they were worried I would bleed out, they were unable to put me to sleep so all they could do was numb the area.

The bigger line worked and I was connected to the Novo Lung. This allowed the doctors more time to hopefully find lungs for me to receive the transplant. After a week on the machine, it suddenly stopped working. Alarms were going off and my oxygen levels dropped dramatically. I started bleeding out but thankfully the doctors and nurses got me linked back onto the machine. I had lost a lot of blood so they had to give me blood and iron transfusions.

I recovered from this and I would still be able to be transplanted if the call came but unfortunately a week later the same thing happened again but I lost a lot more blood this time and had to be given several blood and iron transfusions. The doctors were concerned that if this happened again I would not survive as I was getting weaker each day and they didn't even know if I would be fit to travel over to The Freeman Hospital.

I knew I didn't have long left to live and even planned my funeral with my husband. The hospital was in constant contact with Freeman as they were actively looking for a donor. All I could think was that it's been so long and no transplant, how are they going to find one now, but thankfully on 29th June 2012, a donor was found. I was flown over to The Freeman where I was told the transplant was going ahead as it was a suitable match.

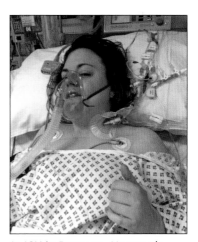

I was so relieved that it was finally happening but also very nervous as I was really sick. 48 hours later I woke up in ICU in Newcastle and couldn't believe I had come through it all. James said the first word out of my mouth was … Florida.

At first I was very confused as I was on a lot of medication and pain killers. After several days I was up on my feet and was even on a sit down bike for the first time in many years.

In ICU in Freeman, Newcastle, after I received that all important gift of life and feeling very grateful.

I had rejection my first week and had several different infections while in the hospital but this was to be expected, which of course was a challenging time.

My biggest step was coming off the oxygen and not needing it. As it was a big part of my life, I was so nervous about coming off the oxygen. I told the doctors and nurses not to tell me when they switched it off, as they were gradually turning it down. One morning a nurse asked me how I was feeling and I said I felt fine. She then told me I had spent the previous night and day with no oxygen on, which I was so shocked and pleased about.

After 5 weeks in The Freeman Hospital, I was fit and well enough to go home but as they say, it's a bumpy road. When I got home I had several infections, CMV being one of them, I ended up in hospital for 6 weeks.

Most of my organs were affected. There was even a mention at one stage I may need a kidney transplant, I had to get injections into my eyes but thankfully the infection cleared. Then I was diagnosed with diabetes but now everything is back to normal.

After it all, I wouldn't change anything, as receiving the transplant has improved my life completely, plus it came at the right time, as the surgeon said I only had a matter of days left to live. I also found out that I was the first patient to be transplanted while on the Nova Lung.

I am now able to do things I could only dream of, I am currently doing my level 3 Nail Technician course and hopefully going to go on to do my Beautician course this year. This is something I wanted to do when I left school but due to my illness I wasn't able to.

I'm now also able to take the dogs a walk which I could never do as I always had to go into a wheelchair, going up a set of stairs or going shopping was so difficult for me. I have even joined a gym which I never thought would happen in my wildest dreams and have started swimming lessons.

Plus we finally had our honeymoon in 2013 which was very emotional as it was always a dream. It came true and just being able to walk around the parks was amazing, I was able to celebrate my 30th Birthday, which all the doctors told me when I was growing up that I may not see. I even booked to go back to Florida to celebrate and we are also currently in the process of adoption as we recently got turned down due to my life expectancy.

Without the generosity of my donor, Gloria and her family and the dedication of the CF team, ICU staff in the Belfast City Hospital and also The Freeman Transplant Team, I wouldn't be here today. The transplant has given me the gift of life and has changed my life in so many ways; it is hard to put into words. I thank my donor and their family from the bottom of my heart.

Me and my husband, James, celebrating my 30th birthday which I never thought I would see.

Above: Me kissing a dolphin which is something I always wanted to do and I finally got the chance to do on our honeymoon (after swimming lessons).
Right: James and myself on our honeymoon in Disneyland, Florida, which we put on hold from 2008 until I received my transplant as I didn't want to come off the list - I wanted to fully enjoy my time without oxygen, etc; finally we were able to go in Nov 2013.

"I think some people don't realise how important it is to sign up to the Organ Donor Register, even my own family, until it was mentioned to me about needing a transplant. I know it's hard for families at the time of them losing someone they love but to give the gift of an organ donation – you are literally saving someone's life and saving another family from losing someone they love."

NHS Organ Donor Register:
0300 123 23 23
www.organdonation.nhs.uk

Marc's Story

Written by Linda McCay (Marc's Mum)

Marc was a healthy athletic boy aged 15, he had never been ill, he was the top goal scorer with his football team. In August 2003 he became a terrible colour, yellowish! He was also breathless so I took him to our local doctor's surgery and they said he had overdone it on holiday; we had recently been to Ibiza.

A mother's instinct is very strong, I put him in my car and took him to A&E at Royal Alexandra Hospital Paisley (where I worked as a Nursing Assistant). I sat outside A & E blasting my horn, the porters came out and put Marc on a trolley. Marc was confused and disorientated! I just kept crying, I knew something was seriously wrong, I had worked in that hospital since 1991 and I just knew...

Every blood test came back deranged! No one could understand why every organ was failing; they were focusing on his liver failure because we had been on holiday!! My son did NOT drink, stereotyped!

That same night, 20th August, Marc was transferred to Edinburgh Royal Infirmary, my mum drove me, we got lost! I just kept crying, this was my baby and I was not in control. When we arrived, doctors and nurses were waiting for us; Marc's heart was failing causing multiple organ failure.

We spent 6 days sitting by Marc's bed, taking turns of quick naps sitting on hard chairs and we were led to believe there was no hope.

Marc started nursery at age 3 in the small village where we come from and he still has the same friends from then. When his friends heard about him, they all arrived, 4 car loads of 16/17 year old boys sobbing, breaking their hearts for their quiet, shy, best pal ever. They were brought to his bed one by one to say goodbye.

Marc was immediately put on life support, ventilator and dialysis. They took him to theatre and let me come in, they tried a catheter up his groin into his heart, they tried a mechanical assist (that was on STV news, first time it had been used in Scotland); it failed. After 6 days of not sleeping, being called round Marc's bed having being told he was dying right there, we were all gathered into a room by Doctor Murray Geddes. He said "Make no mistake,

Marc is dying right now as we speak," (I remember my mum being hysterical). He said "There is a machine in Newcastle which could keep Marc alive until a heart may or may not become available, however Marc may not make it from the bed to the trolley, there is a 99% chance he will not make the journey!"

I begged them to let myself or Marc's Dad be there with him; as there were 9 cardio thoracic staff with him they let Marc's Dad go in one of the two police escorts, they were heading to Edinburgh airport to be met by the RAF. When they were on the runway my husband phoned my daughter who was with me heading to Newcastle. He said the aircraft they had sent was too small for all the staff and all the equipment, so they were going by road. The ambulance only had 2 hours of power left, the Lothian & Borders Police and Northumberland Police shut off the roads and they arrived in record time.

I suffered an anaphylactic shock, my lips and tongue swelled up so badly I was admitted to The Freeman Hospital also! I was met at the doors by one of the transplant coordinators, Anne. Every one of those transplant coordinators are very special people.

After waking up from sedation and large dose of IV antihistamines I went looking for intensive care, I still had the venflon in but I had to find my baby boy. I was shocked when I was met by my other two sons who led me in to see Marc on ECMO. Although I was alarmed by the sight of my son, Neil Wrightson made us all feel positive by his own positivity.

For the first time in days I felt someone knew what they were doing, Transplant coordinator Neil Wrightson was amazing, they were in control, they told us step by step what was happening, what was going to happen and what could happen. Marc was on the top of the register for a heart transplant!

For the first time in 6 days I tried to sleep; that is how much I trusted Team Freeman. I had confidence in them, they were positive when everyone else had been negative! I now trusted someone enough to put my sons' life in their hands.

On 27th August, a heart became available. A boy of 15 had been in a bad car crash. We waited until 3.30am and Neil came back to the wee room outside intensive care where myself, my husband, my two older sons, Darren and Ryan and my daughter, Leasa had been waiting. They were right to the point and explained that the donor heart had been damaged!

I was on an emotional roller coaster! All of this was alien to me and my children, I was feeling their pain also, this was their wee brother; Marc is my 2nd youngest.

On 28th August, lunchtime, another heart, another false alarm, this heart had diseased arteries.

Later on, still 28th August, a perfect match was found; a young boy of 16 had suffered a bleed in his brain, I knew via the transplant coordinator, his name was Martin. The hospital are only allowed to tell you the donor's Christian name because of Data Protection. It is up to the donor's family to give their personal details to the recipient, if they so wish. I found out later that his name was Martin Burton when I contacted Sue and Nigel Burton on DFN.

Marc was taken to theatre at 11.30pm and I paced those corridors the entire night. At 3.40am, I was outside the entrance and saw the blue lights of an ambulance approaching with police escort. A member of theatre staff arrived at the doors, she said "Here comes Marc's new heart!" I was on my knees breaking my heart for that wee boys' family and thanking God for the selfless decision they had made, not knowing then that 11 years down the road myself and Marc would get to meet them, thank them and spend a weeks' holiday in Canada with them.

It would be Marc 16th birthday in 2 weeks' time therefore he was still under children's intensive care. He came out of theatre at 11.30am on 29th

August and was taken to a sterile unit, he was still unconscious, being ventilated. Both his lungs had collapsed and they discovered he had sustained a right sided residual stroke, he had a seizure and had lost 3 stone in weight.

Marc had been unconscious for 3 weeks; he woke up in intensive care hearing all the English accents! He still had the ventilator in so could not ask any questions, from then it was all an uphill struggle but I still had my baby boy.

We spent 4 months in Freeman Hospital and I will never be able to express my confidence in all those skilful, talented people and especially Gareth Parry who has given my son the best care possible.

Marc living life to the full

In Loving Memory of Martin

Written by Susan Burton (Martin's Mum)

Martin was just 16 years of age, a lively happy teenager and living life to the full. He was a real people person, noisy, boisterous, a typical boy. He was also a very caring person and had a wicked sense of humour.

In the early hours of 27th August 2003 Martin suddenly collapsed at home. He staggered into my bedroom with a confused look on his face. He was looking directly at me, but almost through me, as if he couldn't see properly. There was no pain on his face, only confusion. I take some comfort in the belief that he did not suffer as it all happened so quickly and I hope that in his last moments of consciousness he knew that I was there. Unable to rouse him I called an ambulance and he was taken to our local hospital where we were told that he had suffered a brain haemorrhage. He was transferred to Nottingham

My beloved son, Martin.

Queens Medical Centre and taken straight to theatre, whilst our family assembled awaiting news. Sadly, despite the tremendous efforts of the medical profession, within a few hours, we were told that Martin was not going to make it.

Of course this news was devastating to our family. Martin looked peaceful and asleep as he lay in a hospital bed on life support, as we looked on, numb with shock and grief. It was extremely hard and excruciatingly painful to try to accept we were losing him as the Doctors explained the extent of the bleed.

We were subsequently approached by the Consultant who had looked after Martin who asked if we had ever considered organ donation. It was the hardest decision we have ever had to make, to consent to the donation of our child's organs but we agreed immediately, believing without any doubt that Martin would have done so.

Martin was young; his organs were healthy, he had been on no medication and had suffered no injuries. Whatever decision we made was going to make no difference to the situation we were facing, as newly bereaved parents, but by consenting to organ donation we knew that he could make a tremendous difference to the lives of numerous people and their families.

"I felt that if I could save another mother from the journey I knew I had ahead of me I wanted to do so."

The brain stem death tests confirmed what we knew, that although Martin just looked asleep as he was still pink and warm, we had lost him. We were subsequently told that Martin had suffered a huge haemorrhage caused by a congenital condition, an Arterial Venous Malformation of the brain. This had caused no symptoms throughout his short life and for that I am grateful.

We spent the next 36 hours on PICU with Martin. I sat and held his hand for hours, just looking at him and realising that I would never see him alive again. I never moved from his side as I knew how little time I had left with him. There were wires and tubes, monitors continuously bleeping and I tried not to think that Martin was being kept alive for someone else.

News travels very fast and lots of Martin's friends visited him that day to say goodbye. Although I prepared them all as they arrived for how he looked and assured myself that they knew he was dying, they were brilliant and showed then and after, what good friends he had. We were given plenty of time to say our final tearful goodbyes and the retrieval of the organs took place in the evening.

We left the hospital late in the evening, without Martin. Leaving the hospital that night was so hard as I knew I was leaving him behind forever.

Martin's liver was received by a man with a young family. He has been able to work, travel and most importantly see his children growing up.

The recipient of Martin's heart was Marc McCay, a young man who had been given only hours to live. He is now living a full life with his family and friends and we were provided with the opportunity to meet him when both families were invited to join the Rocky Mountaineer Train for Heroes in 2014. It was a very special moment, when, on the banks of Lake Louise, Marc placed my hand on his heart and told me that Martin's was a "perfect heart."

Following Martin's death we became involved in a charity, the Donor Family Network and have been Trustees for a number of years, offering support to other donor families and raising awareness of organ and tissue donation by sharing our story. In many ways the loss of our son has inspired us to do so much. We have spoken to the public on many occasions, assisted with articles in an innumerable number of newspapers, spoken on the radio and even appeared on TV. These have been such positive experiences and have kept Martin's memory alive in so many ways. We attend The British Transplant Games each year, making lots of new friends. We never cease to be amazed at the ability of the athletes who are inspirational in the way they want to honour their donor by doing well and winning medals.

"The world of organ donation has changed our lives and focus. We don't realise what a mighty gift we can give when called on to make a decision about organ donation. Few people will ever have the chance to change someone's world as much as they can at that moment. Martin was able to donate his heart, lungs, liver, kidneys and corneas and we are so proud of him for the gift of life he gave. We know that lives were saved as we have had the honour of meeting two of the recipients."

It is very difficult to come to terms with the loss of a child. Our hearts felt truly broken, time stood still and the pain was physical. I kept expecting Martin to walk through the door; like it had all been a nightmare and I longed to see him, hear his voice and touch him, one more time. I mourned all the things that Martin would miss, learning to drive, girlfriends, a career, travel and children. At first I could not begin to see what we had instead, the good memories of the years he had been with us which can never be taken away. Over time we have learnt to live with our loss, the pain becoming softer and more peaceful. There are always triggers which remind us of the pain we suffered, special times of year which are extremely difficult but we wouldn't want them not to hurt, as that is all part of remembering.

Martin was only with us for a short time and we miss him every day. He lives in our hearts and is in our thoughts every day and we are lucky to have had those growing years with him. We miss his physical presence and always will but we think and speak of him more now with laughter as we remember him as the character he was and in our thoughts will always be.

Love lives on forever
In memory and thought
Of the special ones we loved so much
And the happiness they brought

Love lives on forever
It will never fade away
For in our hearts our loved ones
Are with us every day

Always In Our Thoughts
Forever In Our Hearts

Finally Meeting my Son's Donor Family

Linda McCay (Marc's Mum)

Martin Burton was 16 years old, he had just sat his GCSE's and he wanted to become a nurse. As my son, Marc said, he saved more lives than he could have imagined.

I have wondered, thought about the 16 year old boy from The Midlands whose name was Martin since his heart arrived at The Freeman Hospital at 3.40am on 29th August whilst Marc was undergoing his 12 hour heart transplant surgery.

I initially sent cards and letters however I was determined to find Martin's family to thank them; every life event, every hurdle my son Marc has overcome, I have wanted to thank them and tell them how eternally grateful we all are.

I found them on Donor Family Network as they are both trustees, I then found them on Facebook and via email we chatted.

Last year, Transplant Coordinator, Lynne Holt, contacted Marc and said Nigel and Sue Burton had agreed to meet with us both and we were invited on the trip of a lifetime to Canada; this was myself and Marc's first holiday in 11 years.

At Lake Louise in The Canadian Rockies, we had a Memorial Service and for the first time I mourned properly for Martin, it was very emotional, especially being with Sue and Nigel, they are very special people.

I will never be able to express how grateful we all are as a close family. Marc was dying and I watched my son's system actually shutting down. We were gathered around his bed twice to say goodbye; the pain watching my three sons and daughter being heartbroken was unbearable, therefore the gift of Martin's heart did not just save Marc, I know our family would never have recovered.

With other organ recipients and donor families, Lake Louise.

NHS Organ Donor Register:
0300 123 23 23
www.organdonation.nhs.uk

Yet to see the Bigger Picture of Me

Saadia Sahir Tahir

Breathing: Such an insignificant thing people take for granted.

To breathe one day without nebulisers and steroids, but to breathe on my own.

I have always been independent, strong and active. When younger I did karate, swimming and tennis. I am the eldest of 5; I have 3 sisters and 1 brother so I always had the role of a leader from the start. I was the role model for my siblings which was especially important for my baby sister as she also has CF but thankfully she hasn't been ill like me and here's praying it stays that way.

Unfortunately, this lifestyle only lasted until the age of 10 when I caught Aspergillosis so I was told I had Allergic Bronch Pulmonary Aspergillus. It felt like all my hard work at keeping fit and active was for nothing; the ABPA made my chest tight and made me breathless which didn't help much as I already had Cystic Fibrosis – CF – diagnosed at birth.

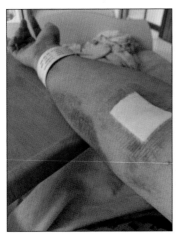

My arm after several attempts at getting a line into a vein for IV antibiotics.

From there my health went downhill; frequent hospital stays for intravenous antibiotics, colds, overnight feeds via a nasogastric tube which I put down every night and took out once the feed was finished – to gain weight. I also needed steroids for controlling ABPA so a lot happened during this time.

At one point I became so ill that because I had no IV access, the situation became so desperate that the decision was made to get emergency surgery to insert a 'Port-a-Cath' to continue antibiotics and this would be better for me in the future as it meant no more being poked like a pin cushion. I was 50/50; I was glad it meant no more needles apart from the one to insert into the Port but anxious too as it wasn't ever talked about or planned.

So over the years, there were ups and downs but I always kept at it to keep healthy so there weren't as many IV's as before getting a 'Port-a-Cath'.

I went to high school but in 3rd year I became so ill that I was in hospital for 10 and a half months, I got out just in time for my exams – I studied hard and passed the exams. I flew through years 5 and 6 and went to college where I did a HND in Admin & Info Management but once again I hit a pothole; I had a slight chest infection but was subscribed oral antibiotic 'Levoflixacillin.' I was put on a high dose and within 3 days my joints were affected so bad that I was bed-ridden; this was such a low time in my life but I made it back on my feet and walking all due to the support of my Nanni, Dad, Brother, Usman and my Sisters, Aisha, Amra and Atyha. My Mum pushed me hard – it is all due to her that today I can walk again. My joints are permanently damaged and weakened which are painful daily so lots of pain killers but I got on with it and still went to work on the weekends in Primark.

Apart from this bump in the road, I achieved my HND and went onto Caledonian University in Glasgow. I completed my degree in Bachelor of Art in Business & Information Management and graduated in Nov 2007.

I worked in Asda for 3 and a half years but eventually I had to leave as my health began to deteriorate due to doing too much. At this point in life my lung function (LF) was 38% – I had never had a LF above 50% but since contracting Aspergillus, my LF went down fast although I still kept going, never sitting at home...always doing something. I used to go to Sunday markets with mum and my brother in early mornings to set up the stall; helping with catering in my parent's business and taking my Nanni out – that was the best part of my life. My Nanni was my best friend; we understood one another and had amazing times together but I have those memories to hold onto – Nanni passed away peacefully on 5th May 2012 with my family and myself by her side.

Nanni's passing was like the ground had swallowed me; life had changed forever. This hit my family and I so hard that to this day it feels like a dream but then we realise Nanni is gone but is watching over us and smiling as she knows we think of her every day and love her forever.

My health went downhill – I think the whole family was depressed – we had kind of just given up and then I was referred to The Freeman to be assessed for transplant. I was told I wasn't ill enough for transplant yet so I was to be seen in 6 months. I continued gaining new skills and did a BABTAC qualification in Makeup for brides.

Over that time my LF went from 24% to 9% and by this time I was on 24/7 oxygen – it didn't help much but in my head I thought it might help tomorrow.

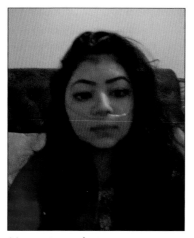

Me pre-transplant.

The second time I went for assessment, I was told it was a YES to being put on the list as I was deteriorating faster than thought – LF was 9%, my Mum, family and I were shocked as we never expected my LF to fall that fast down to 9%. Everything was explained, I was seen by all the people who were going to be involved in the transplant surgery, I read the papers, said a prayer and signed the consent forms.

I received my life-saving call on 24 March 2014 at 00:30.

Complications of getting a line in for sedation made it look like the transplant may not go ahead. But finally 40 minutes after coming from the ward, they got a line in. It was all go.

Surgery took 12 to 13 hours as my lungs 'didn't want to come out.'

I was in ICU for 2 days then moved to High Dependency Ward 38 where I spent 3 days then I was moved to a ward upstairs.

I recovered fast and was anxious and excited to get home to Glasgow. My LF today is 89% and is going up at every clinic review.

I have adjusted to a new eating diet, am keeping fit and healthy which is important whether you have had a transplant or not and I feel amazing.

The whole time my sister, Amra, stayed with me but I sent her home as there wasn't any need for her since the nurses helped me to do things.

My mum and husband were in Pakistan on holiday – they went 3 days prior to me getting my call which is ironic as my husband kept putting off going to go visit my father-in-law as he wanted to be with me at that time and we planned that my mum and brother would go with me but Mum was in Pakistan with my husband, Tahir, my brother had his Master's degree final exam on 25/03/14 so Amra happened to be there and so she came.

It's hard waiting for a loved one in surgery, feeling anxious, time ticking slowly with no news. I appreciate Amra and how she put everything in her life on hold to be there for me in my time of need.

Post-transplant with mum.

I love my sister, my brother and my niece not forgetting mum, dad, my husband, Tahir and my Nanni – all of whom have given me all the happiness, love and continued support that it is so overwhelming.

Me with my husband, Tahir.

I spent my 28th birthday on 14 April on the ward and got home on 17th April, my sister Amra's birthday.

At the time of writing, I am post-transplant 1 year and 5 months. This is a day I never thought I would see as due to my petite size and AB blood type it was going to be hard to get a donor so it may have been a long wait; a wait I didn't have time for. I therefore had decided that I was going to continue life as before and enjoy it and if it was my time to go, I was ok with it.

This is all thanks to my donor and their family as it is a hard choice to make to donate any organs, especially when your loved one has just passed away. I understand how it feels as I have been there with my Nanni but my donor is my hero because without my donor I would not have had the chance for many more fun amazing times with my family, more time to tell them I love them, to see my niece grow up and have a life with her Khala (aunty), plus I am the glue that holds us all together after my Nanni, together we are strong.

I now have the chance to follow my dreams of opening a cake boutique someday, a dream which has started from home whereas before transplant this would still be a dream.

I'm baking, decorating cakes and planning wedding exhibitions and shows which I couldn't do before.

I also met amazing new friends who have made a difference to my life and I'm glad I have them in my life; Kirsty Geddes & Victoria Glen as well as a few more people.

So, that's why it's so important to donate organs and blood as there is someone out there who needs you to save them, once you are gone. So register today and make a difference to someone's family and be a hero.

"I will live my life to the fullest and make this second chance one that will not only make my family proud but my donor and their family too."

From day 1 my parents had been told that I would only live to 15.... in April 2015 I celebrated my 29th birthday so don't give up when you're told it's over because now .....the world has yet to see.... the bigger picture of me.

Oh, and now I can finally say....

'I CAN BREATHE'

Ewan's Second Chance of Life

Written by Ewan's Mum & Dad: Alison & Colin

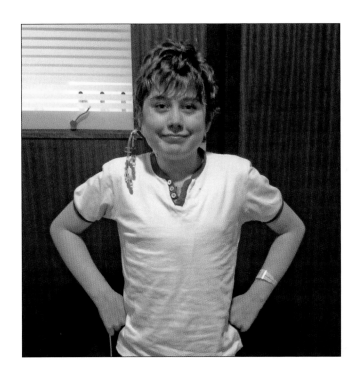

Ewan was born in 1997 and at 18 months old he was diagnosed with Cystic Fibrosis. His life from that point onwards revolved around a vigorous daily routine of chest physiotherapy, nebulisers, medication and a high fat diet together with regular in-patient hospital stays and IV antibiotics.

Ewan stayed relatively well through his determination, our hard work and plenty of exercise until at age 13, his consultant broke the heart wrenching news that he would need to have a lung transplant and arranged for Ewan's first assessment at The Freeman. After two further assessments, a 7 month hospital stay and one false call, Ewan received his life saving double lung transplant on 15 March 2012, at the age of 14. He thankfully sailed through the operation and recovered quickly but had 3 episodes of mild rejection in the first year.

Ewan has not looked back since receiving the gift of life from his wonderful donor and his life is so completely different from what it was pre-

Ewan leading an active life following his lung transplant.

transplant. Even the small things mean so much to all of us, for example he can breathe deeply and easily, he can smell everyday things like cut grass, taste and enjoy his food, run up the stairs and walk several miles. He has embraced life and revels in new adventures which were all out of his reach before the transplant. Ewan has taken up indoor wall climbing and learnt to ski; going to Tackers ski camp twice. He has completed a zip slide across the River Tyne for charity, taken part in The Young Adults Weekend organised by Transplant Sport and competed in 2 British Transplant Games, last year winning 4 bronze medals for ten pin bowling and swimming, for The Freeman Children's Team. He was also nominated for, and won a Special Recognition award at the 2014 Midlands Children of Courage Awards.

Ewan has not let anything hold him back and has had a positive approach to live life to the full, following his transplant. It has been a joy to see him grow stronger and to flourish.

None of this would have been possible, of course, without organ donation and the selfless act of one family, who in their darkest hour allowed their child to become an organ donor and to give Ewan the chance of living a healthy life.

Ewan receiving a special Recognition award at the 2014 Midlands Children of Courage Awards.

"Saying thank you can never express our gratitude enough for saving his life, we are forever grateful to them for keeping our family together and for giving us hope for the future."

Back Home

Paul Ashberry

I can so clearly remember the first night I got back in my own bed after coming home from hospital after the lung transplant.

For many years getting into that bed had involved painful processes which were completely in contrast to the more traditional aims associated with winding down at the end of a day. So I'd regularly put it off, despite mounting exhaustion, as the energy and effort needed to put myself through the steps required were usually impossible to locate. That's not only a reference to the physical staircase, which stood like an impenetrable barrier, but also to the stages of preparation that were involved in getting there. The days of switching off the telly, whacking toothpaste on a brush, throwing clothes in a pile on the floor and crawling into bed had, over the years, become an exercise in nostalgia. For a long time it had required a mammoth feat of determination just to get to the point where I could lie back and flick on the ventilator and oxygen switch – the annoying but reassuring buzz of the equipment would let me know my effort for the day was done.

Returning home after the transplant, the clock was turned back to an earlier stage of life, a time when the ease of getting into bed had been taken for granted. In fact, like with most people, a lack of effort for trivial tasks had too often been taken for granted. That wasn't going to happen anymore. That first night the reality of this new dawn hit home and I promised myself this next chapter was going to be about a different type of life.

My day-to-day existence was something of a whirl in the early stages. I had so many things to do, and people to catch up with, that it was difficult to know what to do first. I had some interesting catch-ups with friends, who wanted to know all the gory details, but who were also genuinely surprised at the transformation that had taken place while I'd been away in Newcastle.

"How you doing?" they'd ask, loading the question with more than the usual casual interest. "It's amazing what they can do isn't it?" I wasn't even sure what amazing thing we were talking about as the subject matter was never clarified. So I agreed it was amazing, in the blind assumption we were talking about transplant surgeons and not magicians, or the accountants of corporate fat-cats.

Once at the stage where my immune system was strong enough, the baby-steps I'd managed in the hospital corridor expanded into the world at large and this coincided with a surge in optimism as I surveyed all the possibilities that lay in front.

I was determined to get fit and treated any movement, regardless of the demands it placed on my body, as contributions to rebuilding core strength. For a while, the scarring and other restrictions meant my all-round mobility was still severely impaired. Like a shark, a tank, or an American car, I was fine when moving in a straight line, but sudden movements, twists or turns had to be avoided.

Getting back home created many similar challenges as my time in hospital, except without the previous inhibited tethering of my movements. My new-found love of walking continued to see an improvement in ability and I had great times rediscovering places I hadn't seen for ages, often craning my neck like an awestruck tourist.

As much as I enjoyed these explorations, the downside was the aches and pains suffered afterwards. In one of the many surreal moments of idle speculation that this period produced, which suggested I was still

Me and my son, Jude, who would never have been born if it wasn't for organ donation – checking out the local culture in Ireland (the second pint wasn't his).

under the lingering influence of some pretty strong medication, this soreness caused me to ponder the possibility that different parts of the body might contain a separate awareness, linked tenuously through the central operating system of the mind; and if this was the case my legs must have been wondering what the hell was going on.

During the years of cocooned existence, my exile from the life that I'd known, when oxygen was often my main companion, these legs had had it easy, slowly wasting away with no idea why they weren't getting used very much but hey, they weren't about to complain – life was good. It was the rest of the body that was taking all the strain. Then all of a sudden without the courtesy of an envoy sent from the brain, it must have felt like they'd been conscripted and roused out of bed with a reveille at six am, then forced to march needlessly and remorselessly, with no explanation given for the change in their circumstances.

The freedom my return home provided made me feel as though everything I ever wanted was there for the taking. It was a dramatic time producing a thrilling sense of how much life can change in a short space of time. It was accompanied by a strong feel-good factor and this probably lasted until my first quote for travel insurance. When I ring an insurance company and they don't make a 'ker-ching' sound when I say the word 'transplant', true freedom can really begin.

Many of the early walks I took were about re-treading old steps, a way of conquering demons, returning to places that held painful memories. With a strange, almost irrational feeling of triumph I'd walk on by, snarling at the floor to prove that it hadn't beaten me: it felt at this point as though nothing could. Despite the lingering emotion of trauma and misery that the location had once caused, I'd returned to show who was boss. But these imaginary conquests and successes over inanimate sections of terrain weren't going to provide fulfilment indefinitely and I had to move things up a notch to maintain momentum.

Looking back now with the knowledge of where this mission to regain fitness was heading, I can feel a sense of pride and even nostalgia about these slow strolls around my local area, but they were only the start of where my new lungs would end up taking me.

Me at the start of The Manchester 10k run (I was nearly overtaken by a walker at one point but I burned him off in the last kilometre.)

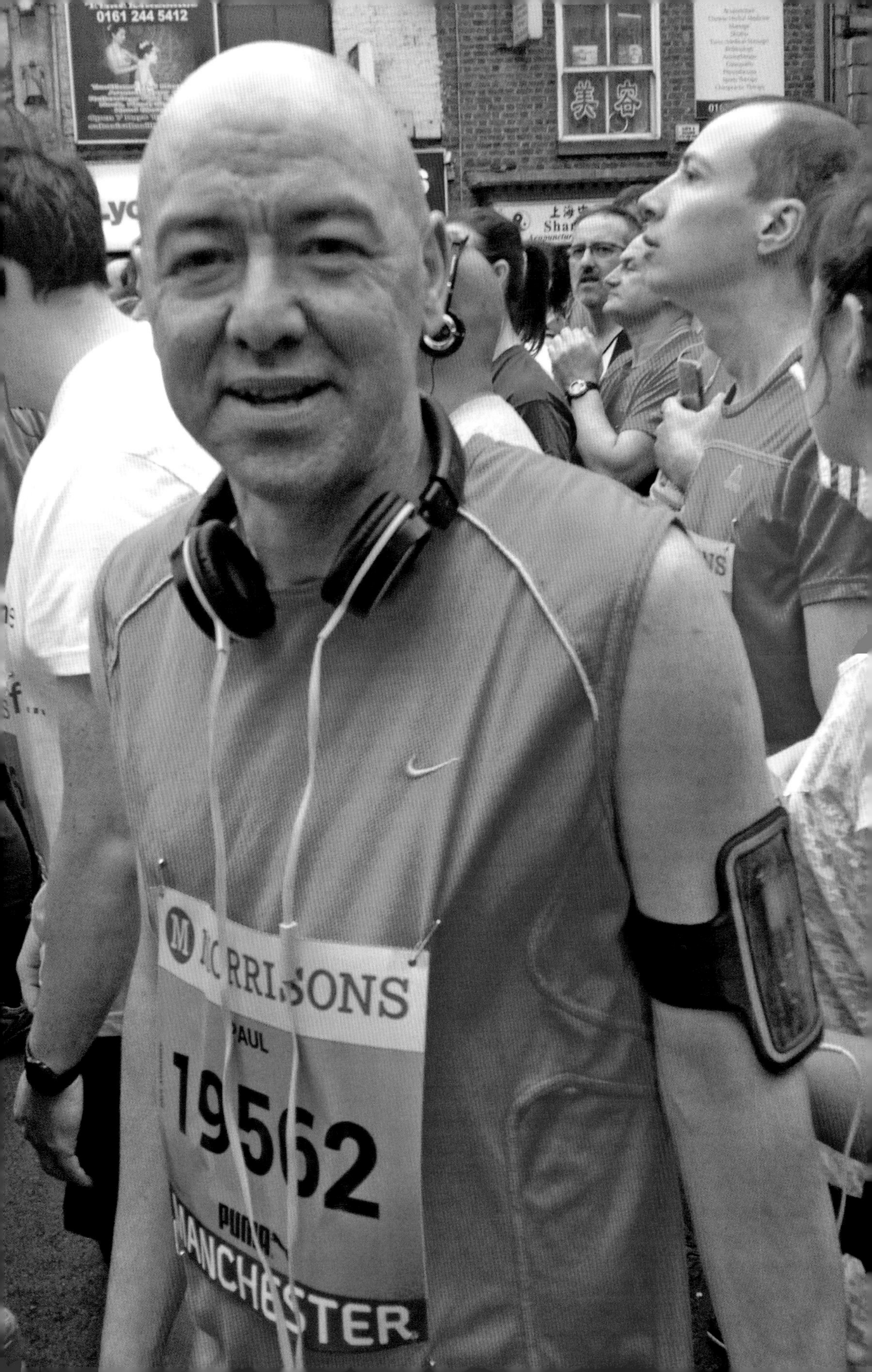
0161 244 5412
PAUL
19562
puma
MANCHESTER

Chance of a Lifetime – Kaylee's Story

Written by Kaylee's mum, Carol Olley

The very beginning…..
Kaylee's remarkable story began at the age of four months old when she was admitted to hospital in what seemed on the surface, to be a meningitis scare. Born a healthy full term baby in April 1987 in Sunderland General Infirmary, she was actually a very easy baby, fed well and was a joy to care for and love. Perfect!

Kaylee was a model baby so when she failed to feed or even show interest in taking a bottle one hot August Sunday, it was uncharacteristic and after an unsuccessful day of trying to ensure she even took water to avoid dehydration, a trip to the GP was organised for the next day to check all was well. The GP suggested she had a chest infection and prescribed antibiotics and Calpol and suggested perseverance was the key. However, a strong believer in 'mothers instincts', I was unhappy with the diagnosis and uncomfortable with the persistent groaning noises throughout the night coming from my baby. On Tuesday morning, following a restless few days for us all, determined to get to the bottom of this problem and also concerned at the lack of fluid taken orally by Kaylee for almost two full days, I prepared to return and challenge the GP.

Ironically, being a teenage mother had its benefits and to this day, I believe that I was a lucky Mum, as on that day my Health Visitor decided to pay a 'spot check' visit. This was routine for young Mum's, just to check they were coping. At 10am, Kaylee was already in the buggy in the lounge ready for the trip to the GP and I was just about to leave my home and walk to the GP Surgery. Hearing a knock at the door, and relieved to see the Health Visitor, I gave a quick resume of the situation, on the doorstep. She came into the lounge and to our shock and horror; Kaylee's lips were turning blue. The Health Visitor took one look and instructed us to get into her car immediately. A quick trip to the GP surgery and a frantic dash to the examination room, suddenly there were people looking at Kaylee and the dreaded word meningitis was mentioned. In no time at all, we were in an ambulance and flying along the motorway with the sirens blazing, back to the hospital where

Kaylee was born.

It was such a surreal situation. On arrival, Kaylee was whisked away and I was led to a waiting room and asked if I wanted to make a phone call to my husband. Soon, he and my Mum arrived but there was no news. The next time I saw Kaylee, it was horrifying to see that she was linked to several IV drips and actually had an IV inserted into her head. Later, I discovered that all her veins had collapsed and it was the only place they could gain access to her bloodstream.

Several torturous hours later, we were told that Kaylee had a problem with her heart. Following an X-ray, it was discovered her heart was so swollen, it almost filled her chest cavity and she was being transferred to The Children's Heart Unit at The Freeman Hospital in Newcastle. It transpired that the reason she wouldn't and couldn't feed was that her heart was failing quickly and she didn't have the strength to even suck and take on food. The groaning noises were literally distress signals as her little body struggled to function as her heart grew weaker and weaker.

We travelled to The Freeman Hospital in an emergency ambulance and I remember travelling over The Tyne Bridge, sirens blaring, with my precious baby in an incubator, clinging to life, as these were the longest moments of my life. On arrival at The Freeman Hospital, again, Kaylee was whisked away and finally, after several hours, we were allowed to see her in the ITU. The sight of my baby on a ventilator, a machine breathing for her and the space blanket covering her to retain her body heat, was terrifying.

The Cardiac Consultant took us to a quiet room and gently explained that we were very, very lucky. In his opinion, without the swift action and the 'motherly instinct' that rejected the initial diagnosis and gave way to the feeling that something was not quite right, he explained that it was highly likely that Kaylee would have died at home in her cot, of heart failure, that night. Kaylee was diagnosed with cardiomyopathy – a viral infection that had attacked her heart. After a week of tests, we were faced with the terrifying news that there was no cure.

Decision Time
I remember being told that heart transplantation was the only option and thinking 'Why me!' Making the decision was easy. Should we give

Kaylee the chance to live or let her die! Simple really! What would you do if this was your baby? Despite the challenges and the high risk, I trusted the transplant team. I remember the two days prior to Kaylee's transplant. We had been told that there was a real possibility that a donor would not be found as baby transplantation just wasn't common so we were prepared for the worst from the very beginning. Even if a heart became available – it was a 50/50 chance of the surgery being successful as she was so tiny. Even then, would she survive after the surgery as the only two other babies transplanted in the UK had died postoperatively several weeks after their surgery. No one even knew if the heart would grow with Kaylee – it was an enormous gamble but one we were willing to take. At the time in the UK, there was a moratorium on baby heart transplantation due to previous failures and the concerns relating to experimental surgery on babies and special permission had to be gained from the then Secretary of State for Health, Kenneth Clarke, to list Kaylee for transplant. I will always be eternally grateful for those who fought behind the scenes to save my baby and allowed her to become the amazing young woman she is today.

The Waiting Game
Waiting for a donor organ was unbearable. Kaylee was initially on a life support machine for the first four weeks and each day, her life hung in the balance, waiting for a chance that may never have arrived. Initial success had been reported in America where several very small babies had received new hearts and were doing well, however, it was so new; these babies were literally only transplanted months before. I felt constantly guilty – I was waiting for a family to lose their child so my child could live. I was praying for a family to make that decision. In hindsight and as many other parents feel this way, I now realise that even though my baby was so desperately poorly, someone somewhere, sadly, would experience what I didn't want to do, regardless of whether Kaylee needed a new heart or not. However that did not stop the pain and guilt at the time. When the call came on 13th October 1987 and the surgery began, I hid in the little waiting room and cried oceans for the family whose baby had died. To this day, I am still very emotional when discussing this particular issue. This will never change.

My saviour throughout all of the madness was the transplant coordinator, Lynne Holt, who held my hand for the whole transplant journey and remains a close friend to this very day. We travelled a whole new journey together as a team, a very close team with no idea of the outcome. The team members include the transplant team, Kaylee, myself, Lynne, Kaylee's stepfather Steve, her sisters Rebecca and Lindsay and our extended family and friends. We are still on this journey today!

Life after Transplant
The news of Kaylee's successful surgery was broadcast on the Reuters news agency world-wide and our insular world was suddenly invaded by world-wide publicity. Sacks of mail, presents and Get Well cards appeared

Kaylee-10 days after transplant with Mum. Copyright Rod Wilson, Newcastle Evening Chronicle.

from all over the World, delivered to The Freeman, addressed to Baby Kaylee. We even received Get Well cards and letters from several inmates at Durham Jail. All are carefully preserved in a special box. Her progress has been monitored and celebrated via birthdays and special occasions both locally and nationally by the media and she is an incredible ambassador for the success of transplantation. The involvement of the local media has been paramount to the campaign as it was The Evening Chronicle 'Operation Heartbeat' appeal that funded the heart transplant programme at The Freeman Hospital in the early days and the campaign to raise awareness by local media has never dwindled. Many local media feel a close bond to Kaylee as they remember when she received her new heart and were part of this amazing unfolding history making event, right here in the North East.

Growing up with Kaylee…….
Who would have thought that 28 years later, Kaylee would be a fit and healthy young woman in the prime of her life, working and playing hard as any young person would do, making the most of each day and importantly-having fun! The impact of her successful surgery had repercussions nationally and internationally as day by day, month by month and year by year, she grew up in the glare of the media and under the watchful eyes of the medical professionals who saved her life with their courage and determination. Transplantation creates miracle stories every day

however the heroes are the donor families who selflessly give to others with no gain for themselves.

Above left: Kaylee with transplant coordinator Lynne Holt and hospital staff, 21 years after saving her life. Abover right: Kaylee at Tyne Bridge, Photo courtesy of Peter Berry, Sunderland Echo. Bottom left: The Davidson Girls – Lindsay, Kaylee and Rebecca – Bridesmaids at Mum and Stepfather's Wedding, April 2007, Mauritius.

"Each and every day, I give thanks to the family whose brave decision utterly changed my life and gave life to my child. There is no greater gift. Thank you is such a small word and just never seems to quantify how I feel as a mum. A stranger, whom I have never met, gave the most precious gift, the gift of life, to my very own baby. I owe a huge debt to this family and I am forever grateful, each time I look at Kaylee. On each anniversary, amongst the celebrations, my family and I spend reflective quiet time remembering the amazing family who made this possible. Maybe we will meet one day!"

Christopher's Story

Christopher Richardson

My name is Christopher Richardson. On July 27th 2007, I had my lifesaving heart & lung transplant following 22 years of ill health because of a serious heart problem since birth.

Left: Me before my transplant.
Right: Me 8 years post heart & lung transplant.

Now 8 years down the line, I can do things I thought would never be possible like going to Newcastle United matches and going to race meetings.

I play darts competing in The British Transplant Games representing The Freeman Team.

I can now walk without getting tired or out of breath.

"All thanks to My Donor who I always think about."

A Series of Poems

by Chris Goldthorpe Wormald

I had my double lung transplant 16th January 1996

BEAUTY I HAVE WITNESSED

Once upon a time I didn't know who I was
But now I'm awake and that is because
All the beautiful people that I've met and have witnessed
on my journey through this life
In bad health or fitness
For what I have seen I know I've been blessed and I also have to
write it down
You know!
Get it all off my chest
So I as I move forward and hope to witness so much more
It all feels right as it did once before

Chris W 5/5/14

I BELONG

I'm starting to feel!
But losing my touch
I'm going back to a time
That I once loved so much
Back to a time I was happy and free
Back to a time where I long to be
And I have no fear of what is to come
Because I have the power
And I know I belong.

Chris W 6/8/14

PASSING THROUGH

Death brings sadness
But yet it should not
We all have a place
But here it is not
This beautiful planet
Has helped us grow
But soon it will be time
For us all to go
Back into the stars
Where we were all born
We all have a destiny
So here to earth we were drawn.
So please do yourself and humanity a favour
Live a true honest life
And you will reap fruits for your labour.
So if death creeps up
On someone you know
Just send them your love
So they can still grow
Your love as light will reflect, and the receiver
Shall never forget.
So when death appears
Rejoice their life be happy not sad
Remember they're on their way home & for that they'll
be glad.

Chris W 25/07/14

My Personal Journey

Colin Arthur

I remember those very words, it was a warm summer's day in 2003 and my visit to the hospital was for test results to see if I had the genetic disease Common Variable Immunodeficiency. The words my respiratory consultant spoke were so daunting. To be told I had the deficiency, added to my already known history of COPD and genetic faulty gene, Alpha1 antitrypsin deficiency, left me empty.

Then when he said "We will have to, at some point, consider you for lung transplantation". The most frightening words I had ever been told, I was only forty two years of age! Of course as you can imagine, both my wife and I, who I had only married eight weeks prior to this news, were sat in shock. Then I asked him, " You mentioned I will need a transplant – when is 'some point'?" His reply was, "Possibly when your around fifty five years of age." That seemed so long away and I felt somewhat relieved. Little did I or the doctors know how quick my health would then start to deteriorate.

It was now 2004 and the chest infections began to get worse, I was getting more breathless and because of the immunodeficiency, my body wasn't producing the antibodies to fight off infection. I was at this point travelling to St James Hospital for intravenous immunoglobulin replacement every three weeks. It helped to fight off infections for so long, however, they were ongoing and that's when the hospital visits started to be more frequent; I had to spend more time as an inpatient on the respiratory wards. I was also told by the doctors that going to work, in my profession, was now out of the question. I was in construction and with the dust, weather elements and the physicality of the work, it had to end. By the back end of 2004, I was on oxygen therapy throughout the night, this then turned into being 24/7 after a stay in hospital in early 2005 because of an exacerbation of COPD where I was in intensive care for two days. Eventually I got home and my wife was now my fulltime carer as I was becoming so breathless and could only function with oxygen, whatever I was doing. It felt like my life was starting to fall apart and now depression started to kick in. We, as a unit, battled on and Rach, my wife, became a rock in helping me overcome some of my obstacles. The year 2005 passed with several more stays in hospital and my lung function continued to deteriorate more and more.

Above: Myself and Rachael on holiday, Stapleford Park, Melton Mowbray, June 2005.

We were now into 2006, this became the darkest year of all, for us. I was now constantly in hospital, my weight had dropped by nearly three stone; I was now well under ten stone and could feel myself getting weaker by the day. I was even using a Bi pap machine throughout the night as my breathing was so poor. I was so ill and my lung function was getting so bad that now the only option was for a lung transplant. I had been in and out of intensive care and was classed as being at the end stage of COPD. I had signed a form to say 'do not resuscitate' if I had another exacerbation as they said I would only have a 1% chance of survival. I eventually got a date for September to go for a transplant assessment but was in hospital and they were worried I wouldn't be able to go, I was so ill. My doctors did everything they could in order to get me to the assessment at Freeman Hospital and I was taken from my hospital bed up to Newcastle by ambulance and was put on the urgent list for lungs, not only in the UK but Europe as well. My lung capacity was at 13% when I went on the list. I had to get my house in order and sign a live will, they said I wouldn't make Christmas.

I was dying at this point and the hospital could do no more. I got through Christmas 2006 but it was bleak. Then the phone rang on January 3rd 2007 and it was the transplant co-ordinators, I was told to be ready, which we were, as we had a bag packed from the day of my assessment. We waited and the call came back, it was a no-go, the lungs weren't good enough.

On 6th March 2007, I was at home and just holding on, my wife had gone to see friends, her first night out for months. McMillan nurses were caring for me whilst Rach had respite when the phone rang at 7pm. The co-ordinator said "An ambulance is on its way for you and will be at your home by 8pm, we have some lungs and will do tissue match upon arrival." I was blue lighted up to Freeman and by midnight I was gowned up and had pre meds. There were two of us waiting, it was now about tissue match. It then got to 2am and I matched. The co-ordinator then said "I'll see you on the other side, good luck." My bilateral lung transplant was happening; the next thing I recall was waking up on 14th March 2007.

I was left in a induced coma for 6 days as I was taking in too much carbon dioxide, however, when I did wake, my wife had sat by my side since the transplant and greeted me with a huge smile. I was breathing on my own.

This was the first day of breathing on my own and without oxygen, the rehabilitation was hard work with physiotherapy, however I arrived home for my 46th birthday at the beginning of April. Before I knew where we were, it was Christmas and did we celebrate!

There were a few early blips with acute rejection but 2007 passed by and I was feeling great about life again. It was great to go outdoors and walk my dog, taking in everything you normally take for granted, the wildlife, parents and children playing, the countryside – the list was endless. We even had a holiday at one of the Greek islands.

Things were good again for us as husband and wife. Each time I visited clinic the numbers were good with lung function and x-rays and the bronchoscopies were all ok. I did a letter for my donors' family, to thank them and tell them that I would always have their family member, who gave me the gift of life, constantly in my thoughts. All I know is the donor was male, aged 42 and the lungs came from Brussels. The transplant coordinators sent the letter to the family although I heard no more after that.

We were having regular holidays away again and the only thing I had to be careful of was to ensure I took the medication and be monitored at the hospital. No more oxygen, no more anxiety; feeling positive again.

I couldn't go back to work as I still had the immunodeficiency and was still very prone to infections and at times became breathless. Then in 2011 my lung function began to drop. I was taken in for another bronchoscopy and back to clinic a few weeks later for other tests. I was told I was in chronic rejection, the readings on the lung function tests showed this clearly. It wasn't significant enough to get worried, but it was happening. Medication was changed slightly and things continued and it dropped a little more, so we started to spend time in Spain where the climate was better and we did this up until 2013. We were out one night and I ended up in Cartagena Hospital following a blackout I had. I had a severe infection and the doctors

On holiday on the Island of Lesbos.

in Spain would not let me fly back until the test results were back which took at least 10 days! We arrived back in the UK in April 2013 and I went straight into hospital once I got home. My black out was due to medication and my lung function had dropped even more. There was a history of heart problems in the family so more tests were done. My lung function had dropped significantly enough now for the transplant clinic to decide which way to go. Even though I was still feeling ok I would get breathless upon walking about 200 metres and felt constantly tired.

In 2014 I was sent for some routine tests to the Royal Victoria Hospital in Newcastle to see if acid reflux was going back into my lungs; I had these tests in 2012 but they all came back negative for reflux. Any way, I had the endoscopy and special tilt x-rays etc; it was decided that I did have acid reflux which may be the cause of my drop in lung function. Another operation was fixed for July 2014 where they did what is called a Nissen's fundoplication; through key hole surgery they remove a small piece of your intestine to stop acid going into the lungs, but back into your gut. This was done and they said it would take a while to show any signs of success. I have had several visits to clinic since and now I can happily say as of June 2015 things have levelled out, I have chronic rejection (obliterative bronchiolitis) as the team call it. It's not going to go away, but as I asked the Professor "How am I now?" His reply, "You're steady away."

That was all I needed to know.

"As any transplant patient, no matter what the transplant is, we all exchange one set of problems for another. What is so important from all of this, is, without the message to carry the card, or register on the donor website, we would have no donors, no transplants and most of all, no gift of life. It's so important this work can carry on, as the team up at Freeman have been and are amazing. Thank you so much for the gift of life. Many thanks for reading my story."

Rachel's Transplant Journey

Writen by Eve Hooley, Rachel's mum

January 2012, we took Rachel to our local GP as she was a little under the weather, they said Rachel had a heart murmur and booked her in to see a specialist in a months' time. However, over the next 24 hours Rachel took a turn for the worse and was admitted to The Freeman Hospital. Over the next 4-5 hours, test after test was carried out. Rachel was chatty and happy. For the first time a cannula was put into Rachel. Up till this point in Rachel's life, the only medicine she had taken was Calpol. Rachel started to get upset and very tired.

I couldn't take in what was happening and still expected to be home that night. It was hard watching my child, not having any answers. One of the consultants came to see my husband Michael and I and took us into a room away from Rachel. This was when I knew it wasn't going to be as simple as giving her a few tablets and sending us home. He sat us down and said, "I am sorry to say Rachel has dilated cardiomyopathy." He went on to say, at this point, they didn't know why, but they would do all they could to slow it down.

A heart transplant was mentioned but it never crossed my mind that Rachel would need this. Words didn't come; my mind was all over the place. How could my 7 year old daughter have heart failure? My head was a mess. I sat with Rachel, held her hand, looked into her beautiful, blue eyes and told her that her heart was poorly and that everyone was going to try and make it better. Rachel looked at me and smiled. (A smile that would get us through all this).

From that day, Rachel's body was pumped with so many drugs through a cannula, injections into her legs, oral medication which Rachel had never taken before and each day they increased the medicine. Rachel had a Hickman line to administer the drugs. As heart failure took over and Rachel became weaker and weaker, an NG tube was fitted to give her nutrients and milk to build her up. At this point she was placed in HDU. Her life was slipping away before our eyes. Rachel never questioned anything that was happening to her. She looked at the whole experience as an adventure. She loved playing with the play specialist and playing on the Wii with the Clown Doctors.

Rachel had been in hospital 3 weeks by now and I could see she wasn't getting any better. I could see my daughter wasting away before my eyes. It was the most horrific thing to see. The bones appearing, the lack of interest, not wanting to play was soul destroying but Rachel kept us all going, she would lie in bed playing on the Wii with the Clown Doctors, still managing to smile and laugh.

It was the 1st of February, Doctor Richard Kirk, one of the cardio consultants took us into the parent's room, with one of the nurses. Being taken into this room normally meant news that we didn't want to hear. I could see by the look on Doctor Kirk's face that today was no different. He sat us down and said that time was running out, Rachel didn't have much longer and all that was left was to place her on the Organ Donor List and hope a heart would come in time. Doctor Kirk went through the statistics that 1 in 3 die waiting, as there aren't enough donors available.

I knew in my heart that he was right; I knew Rachel didn't have much longer. Her body couldn't take much more. We agreed for Rachel to be placed on the Organ Donor List. Doctor Kirk explained that Rachel was to be placed at the top of the European list as she was now so ill. My whole world fell apart. Inside, my heart was breaking knowing that time was running out and that for Rachel to live another family must go through the loss of their loved one, something I didn't want to have to go through.

I walked back to see Rachel in HDU and thought, how do I tell her this? How do I tell my daughter she needs a new heart? I just didn't know how to do this. But once I walked into the room and looked at Rachel smiling, I climbed onto the bed, looked in to those blue eyes, held her thin, tinny body and told her that her heart was so poorly and to get better she needed a new heart. Rachel looked back at me, smiled and said ok. I don't think she had enough energy or ability to say any more than that.

After being listed for 9 days, on Thursday 9th February, Rachel's life was hanging in the balance; she was so poorly that the decision was made to take her to PICU and be placed on a life support machine. This would give everyone time to decide what options were left. I remember holding Rachel and explaining that her heart was so poorly that it had to have a rest and the only way to do this was to put her into a special sleep. Rachel just looked at me and smiled, and held my hand. She was so calm and all I wanted to do was scream and cry. The walk to PICU felt unreal and every part of me never wanted that walk to end. I kissed Rachel and wondered if this would be the last time I would see her amazing blue eyes.

The next time I saw Rachel she had wires and tubes all over her body and she was on a life support machine, I sat and read stories and held her hand.

The next day on 10th of February at 7pm, Michael had just left PICU for the night. I was sitting reading to Rachel when one of the PICU doctors walked in crying. Everyone seemed to be crying. He said they had a heart for Rachel, a perfect heart.

I stood up not knowing what to say, then a wave of sadness came over me and I started to cry, not for Rachel but for her donor and donor family, for I knew they had made, during their saddest time, the hardest decisions to donate their loved one's organs. They had said goodbye to their loved one. No one can really explain all these emotions going around, sorrow, happiness, loss, relief, guilt.

I phoned Michael and told him the news and he too started to cry and said he would be on his way to The Freeman Hospital.

We walked to theatre with The Transplant Team and Rachel. Mr Hassan was to be carrying out the transplant and Neil Wrightson was The Transplant Coordinator. We both kissed Rachel and I knew I would get to see those blue eyes again and that contagious smile.

The transplant took 6 hours and we were able to see Rachel in PICU in isolation and I was amazed to see that she was awake, sleepy but awake. She was moving around and trying to take out the breathing tube. She was showing her normal determination to recover. When we walked in she tried to smile, she looked so small and fragile but she was alive.

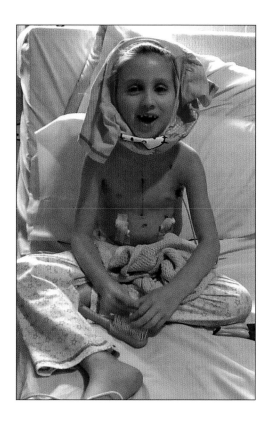

Rachel was only in PICU a few days after her transplant then back to the ward. She then had to start to get used to taking a lot of medication at set times and also living with the knowledge of having a new heart and where it came from. Rachel was only in hospitals three weeks after her life saving heart transplant then we got to take her home and to be a complete family again.

Rachel makes me smile as I remember talking to her about her heart and where it came from. She was just so grateful and looked at me and said "My donor is wonderful." From that day on Rachel has never forgotten her donor and releases a balloon at the Angel of the North on the 10th of February as a mark of remembrance every year.

> ## "Our family would not be complete today if not for organ donation, if not for a truly wonderful family saying YES to organ donation during their hardest time."

Rachel has competed in three British Transplant Games, winning medals in all of them and in one World Winter Transplant Games in France representing GB and took part in The Nicholas Cup. She had an amazing time and came 5th for GB in the slalom race BUT was awarded The Nicholas Cup. Rachel is the first ever GB child to win the cup.

When I look at Rachel, I feel so much love for her but I also see in her the love another family had for their loved one, so much love that they had the ability to say yes to Organ Donation and share that love around.

Organ Donation has kept my family compete, I hope by reading this it shows you how important Organ Donation is and how it is truly the most wonderful gift you can give to someone.

"Rachel's donor and donor family are in all our hearts and they will never be forgotten. We owe them so much and thank you will never be enough."

NHS Organ Donor Register:
0300 123 23 23
www.organdonation.nhs.uk

Hearts That Matter UK

Hearts That Matter UK was set up by Kate and Rachel Hooley in March 2014. Rachel, who had undergone a life-saving Heart Transplant at The Freeman Hospital and her sister Kate who had watched her sister's life slipping away before her eyes before a truly wonderful family had said yes to Organ Donation.

The Freeman Hospital is one of only two centres that carry out children's heart/lung transplants in the country.

Rachel and Kate set up Hearts That Matter UK to promote Organ Donation and to show the positive impact organ donation has on a whole family; to spread the word to as many people as possible so that more families can stay complete like ours. To encourage others to join The Organ Donor Register and to make sure people know the importance of sharing their wishes with their loved ones.

www.organdonation.nhs.uk

'Without the organ donor, there is no story, no hope, no transplant. But when there is an organ donor, life springs from death, sorrow turns to hope and a terrible loss becomes a gift.'

Kate and Rachel

Save a Life,
Be an Organ Donor

They also want to support as many charities across the country as possible; charities that offer support, guidance and unforgettable memories for children and their families. They wanted to give something back to the charities that have been there for them.

They do this by selling, on their Facebook page and Twitter, their handmade bracelets and handbag charms with all money going direct to the Children's Heart Unit Fund (Chuf) the charity attached to Ward 23, clinic E and the Paediatric Intensive Care Unit, Freeman Hospital.

They also donate bracelets and handbag charms to charities across the country for them to sell at events and promotions, to keep all the money raised from doing this.

Charities they have supported so far are:

- Chuf
- Well Child
- FHLTA
- Heart Transplant Families UK
- North East Hearts & Goals
- Children's Heart Federation
- Tackers

Hearts That Matter UK also attend events throughout the year promoting Organ Donation.

Kate and Rachel just want to make a difference and to live their lives to the FULL...

Register to join the NHS Organ Donor Register today

It takes less than 2 minutes

Age and existing medical conditions are not a barrier –
Anyone can join

Online: www.organdonation.nhs.uk

Phone: 0300 123 23 23

Most importantly, discuss your wishes with your family and friends

The Role of the Cardiothoracic Theatre Team in Transplantation

Sharon Barnes

The theatre team is often the invisible link during a patient's recovery from illness however in the case of the team based within Cardiothoracic Theatres at Freeman Hospital, they began as, and remain an integral and integrated part of the whole process of transplantation. It is because of the unique relationship the whole team has built and still works hard to maintain that the unit continues to perform a record number of transplants and break new barriers in the history of transplantation.

After qualifying as a State Registered Nurse in 1981, I remained at the Royal Victoria Infirmary until moving to Newcastle General Hospital in 1983. Following a brief time gaining the experience I thought would provide me with a good foundation to start planning how I wanted my career to develop, I decided the time was right to pursue my passion which was theatre nursing, and when the opportunity arose in 1984 to join the team in Cardiothoracic Theatres at The Freeman Hospital, I was delighted. I had no idea that over 30 years later I would still be part of the team responsible for providing patients with the 'Gift of Life' following transplantation. My first visit to Cardiothoracic Theatres, however, was in 1979 when I worked as a student nurse on ward 7, now ward 23 and was given a brief glimpse into the lives of children and their families born with congenital heart defects.

I can still remember the news of the first successful human heart transplant performed by Christiaan Barnard in 1967 and can remember thinking this was something other people did, never entering my mind that one day that would be me and even today I am filled with a wondrous feeling of amazement that I was involved in the beginning of the transplant programme at Freeman Hospital and also directly involved in many of the significant milestones the team were responsible for, not only in Newcastle but Europe and beyond.

Building the transplant programme at Freeman Hospital and specifically the team within Cardiothoracic Theatres was always more than our job; it was our vocation and passion. Everyone involved gave up their own time to be involved in all aspects including helping raise funds by participating in charity events through the campaign 'Operation Heartbeat.' As a team we all felt part of the programme and had a sense of being its guardian with a duty to be responsible for ensuring its success for the patients who were to benefit from receiving a transplant. It would be true to say we were and remain extremely proud of our achievements both within Freeman Hospital and within our region.

I began my career as a staff nurse in Cardiothoracic Theatres and ended it when I retired in November 2014 as matron and although my contribution and part played changed over the years, I was still extremely proud of my team still being able to meet the challenges of providing the service 30 years later, 365 days a year, 24 hours a day, with the same enthusiasm, dedication and duty of care for our patients. No matter what time of day or night, the team demonstrates the same confident, reassuring and sense of celebration for the recipients whose lives we were about to change as well as thoughtful consideration and respect for the donors and their families whose generosity and courage gave someone a second chance of life.

The theatre team is often described as one of the finest examples of the definition of working as a team; everyone knows, understands and respects everyone's part and contribution to the whole process. Communication is often through a sense of just knowing and intuition and for the theatre team in Cardiothoracic Theatres at Freeman consisting of nurses, technicians, surgeons, anaesthetists and cardiologists often having worked with one another over decades, the skills and expertise has produced a phenomenal team with the knowledge and skills to continue passing onto others the sense of pride and ownership of what is a successful and sustainable transplant programme.

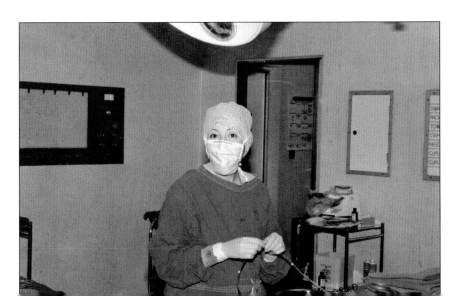

Co-ordinating Transplants

Lynne Holt

I first became involved in transplantation 36 years ago as sister-in-charge of The Intensive Care at Papworth Hospital, Cambridge. The first UK heart transplant programme had started at the hospital only months before my arrival and I was responsible for caring for the newly transplanted patients.

They were exciting and challenging times in those early days of heart transplantation. I became very involved and soon realised I wanted to specialize in this field. Transplantation continues to be challenging and there are new developments all the time.

One of the Surgeons, I worked with, Christopher McGregor, went to Stanford, California to learn more about Heart and Lung Transplantation. One of his patients, Bill Hewlett, of Hewlett Packard Computers, heard about Chris's plans to start a heart transplant programme at The Freeman Hospital in Newcastle and he gave Chris the money for the first 3 heart transplants!

The first heart transplant was performed in May 1985 on a local lady from Gateshead, Pauline Duffy. Pauline lived for 25 years and saw her children grow up.

The Chronicle Newspaper Group started a fundraising campaign called Operation Heart Beat which funded the next couple of transplants and then the government recognised The Freeman Transplant Programme as the third funded centre, following on from Papworth and Harefield.

I was then appointed as the first Clinical Transplant Coordinator in the UK and I moved to The Freeman Hospital in Newcastle 29 years ago, to co-ordinate the transplant programme for heart and lung transplantation in both children and adults.

My role involved coordinating the whole transplant process from when the patient is referred for assessment, joins the waiting list, to receiving offers of organs, organising the theatre teams, retrievals and supporting the patients and their families throughout the whole transplant journey; a great mix of clinical, organisational, management and communication skills. Coordinating a retrieval that proceeds to transplant is always rewarding, exhilarating, emotional, exhausting and always humbling however nothing compares to what the patient and families experience!

> "I have always believed that we can all, in our own individual ways, commit to making a difference. I am grateful to all my patients and families who have made a difference to my life."

Recognising that patients and families need support throughout the whole transplant journey, in early 1987, I booked an upstairs room of The Three Mile Inn, Gosforth and organised a meeting for patients and families to discuss a support group. I asked Eric James, no. 4 heart transplant, to chair the meeting and hence The Freeman Transplant Association (FTA) was born.

Over the last 29 years, I have been privileged to work with an amazing team. I have been part of many 'firsts' at The Freeman Hospital – longest surviving baby heart transplant – Kaylee, first double lung, first heart/lung, first single lung, heart and single lung, heart and liver, lungs and liver, heart and kidney, different generation artificial heart pumps, ex vivo lung machine, the nova lung bridge to transplant, etc;

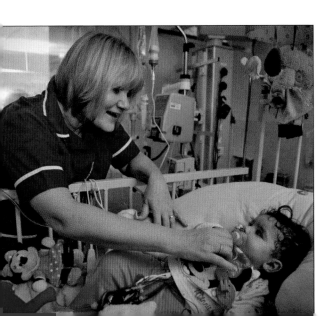

I first took The Freeman Team to The British Transplant Games in 1987 and the first Children's Team in 1989.

I am passionate about raising awareness of organ donation and discussing one's wishes with their families.

How Did It All Start?

Professor Paul A Corris

In May 1986, I found myself sitting in my office one morning having just been appointed as a Consultant Specialist Respiratory Physician at The Freeman Hospital in Newcastle, planning the rest of my day. The heart transplantation program in Newcastle had just celebrated its second birthday under the leadership of Chris McGregor and I had seen a number of heart transplant recipients with respiratory complications following heart transplantation. It seemed like an exciting new area. Lung transplantation was globally in its infancy. There were very few centres worldwide and received wisdom at that time was that successful surgery necessitated heart lung transplantation. Then Toronto published a small series of successful outcomes in six patients following single lung transplantation for patients with lung fibrosis.

There was a knock at my door. Little did I know what a profound effect the conversation that took place on my subsequent career. It was Chris McGregor. "How do you fancy starting a lung transplant program in Newcastle with me?" he said. I had no hesitation. "Sounds like a sound idea," I replied.

"We need to visit Toronto and find out how to look after the patients. I can do the surgery," he said with typical surgical confidence.

So off to Toronto we duly went. It was a six day visit and very memorable for several reasons. Firstly, we realized we could do all the things Toronto had suggested was critical to success so that was satisfying and confidence building. Secondly, I found myself feeling most unwell whilst there and arrived home feeling dreadful with a single spot on the front of my chest. Next day I was swamped with chicken pox lesions.

Unknown to me I had not had chicken pox as a child and it subsequently became clear that I had caught it from my son just before leaving for Toronto. I was highly infective whist there so could have wiped out the world's first group of lung transplant recipients who of course were immunosuppressed. Thankfully none of the patients came to harm. Phew!

Well Chris and I set about building an ace team and in 1987 we performed Europe's first successful single lung transplant. The brave recipient was a brave Sunderland lass called Dorothy Graham and she lived for 18 years so we started pretty well!

As ever it was amazing to see the confidence and trust that patients were prepared to invest in us and that has sustained all of us during the subsequent development of Newcastle and its recognition as a World expert centre for lung transplantation. It has been a privilege to look after all our patients and a source of strength for us all.

My own career, then, was shaped following a short conversation in May 1986 and I can honestly say that it shows the value of keeping your mind open to new developments and giving full commitment and energy to what you do in the medical field. It's been an absolute ball and certainly if I was in the same position my answer to Chris's question would have been the same. "Sounds like a sound idea."

A Transplant Journey

Dr Gerard Meachery

"Why don't you come over to Newcastle and have a
look before you decide where you are heading..........."

Little did I know that those seemingly simple few words uttered to me by
the highly energetic and indefatigable Professor Paul Corris would have
such a profound impact on me and my whole family. I was fortunate
to have had a tremendous training experience in Dublin with very
inspiring mentors who had trained
all over the world and brought their
expertise back to Ireland. I had first
met Professor Conor Burke as a final
year medical student at the Royal
College of Surgeons Medical School
in Ireland when he had returned
from his training in Stanford
University during the exciting era
of Heart and Lung transplantation
and would regale us with stories
of his transplant experiences in the
United States. Few people know he
is credited by the ISHLT with being
the first to describe chronic lung
rejection. He first showed me how
to perform a bronchoscopy in 1993 and little did he or I know then,
that his experience in Stanford which he passed to me, would be further
honed in subsequent training experiences and is now being passed on
to our trainee doctors at the Freeman. He once introduced me to his
mentor in Stanford, Jim Theodore, the Medical Director of the Heart-
Lung and Lung Transplant programme in Stanford who was a warm and
truly inspiring figure.

Lung transplantation was at its very infant stages of development in
Ireland and I recall an early meeting with Paul and Neil Wrightson in the
basement of the Mater hospital in Dublin where they were setting up a
partnership lung transplant arrangement with the Freeman. Neil and I
often reflect on how strange to look back to those early years to see this
come full circle.

I recall my first experience of a heart transplant operation in the Mater hospital and was hooked immediately. Even today I still try to get to the operating theatre with our tremendously skilled surgeons at the Freeman when I get a chance – it truly is a remarkable operation which is becoming increasingly more complex and challenging. I also came to value and appreciate the tremendous expertise of the intensive care and nursing team who I trained with in Dublin who had brought their varying experiences from Australia, the UK and the USA to benefit the patients we looked after. The teamwork and work ethic (6.30am starts on a normal working day were the norm) didn't bother us – it was being part of something special that would radically alter the life of a person – not just "a patient" but someone's child, spouse, parent or grandparent. I was in awe watching the heart start to beat and even more to get that patient back to normal daily activities very quickly. This dedication in our nursing and co-ordinator staff is a constant at the Freeman and is a reflection of the commitment of the whole team involved at every level that makes this process work as there are so many uncertainties that come especially with lung transplantation. There are so many factors we cannot account for in addition to the environmental exposure but at the same time, this is a chance to live and get on with your life, as patients can't live in a bubble and nor would they want to.

I had continued my respiratory training in Cystic Fibrosis again working with an inspiring and dedicated man, Professor Gerry McElvaney who brought his expertise back from his experience over a decade in North America. He lived and "breathed" CF and alpha one anti-trypsin deficiency and was obsessive in his passion to find a cure. Sadly as in other units around the world, many would succumb to their illness before being able to get a transplant. We worked together to set up a unit in North County Dublin with so little resource, in addition to running a medical school curriculum and respiratory service. Again, I couldn't complain as we were part of something we truly believed in and he worked even longer hours than most of the junior doctors and continues to do so. Nevertheless being enthusiastic and (probably foolishly) idealistic provides the drive to make this work towards a better life for the patients who needed us.

I recall a wonderful young man who would hitch a ride on a lorry to get to our clinic. I still recall the different coughs emanating from the various rooms on the CF ward when we started rounds in the morning (incidentally it is something that intrigues many CF patients and their families after a lung transplant when the room is silent in the mornings as the cough is no more). However, despite the workload, endless hours and sleepless nights, it is where I met my future wife (over a chest x-ray on call) who shared the same passion for patient care and teaching, and supported me all the way in this dream to do something special for those who desperately need a chance to live a longer and hopefully a better life despite all the serious challenges of lung transplantation. This was especially difficult when I made one of the hardest decisions of my life to leave her and our 3 month old baby behind in Dublin and go to Newcastle despite many friends, family and mentors telling me I was mad to pursue this as my future would be even more uncertain. It was a challenge living apart for over 2 years but she stood by me despite the tremendous toll on her too.

And this brings me back to the first statement – what began as a casual chat with Paul Corris over a drink at a meeting in Ireland, developed into discussions about career plans which culminated in the suggestion of, "Why don't you come over to Newcastle and have a look before you decide." He subsequently came back again to Dublin and charmed my wife

over dinner – he's very good at that! I guess I had sold my soul to Newcastle by then.

We knew we would have to leave Ireland at some stage as we had reached the limit of our positions there and we were considering options in North America and the UK. It also had to be a place where we both could pursue our desire to make a difference (she is a tremendously talented and dedicated Neurologist) and importantly build a life for our children. Our first visit to Newcastle together made the decision easy as we first encountered the tremendous friendliness of the people here as well as the charm of the city and the countryside. There are some days (especially the bitter winters in the North East) that I do wonder how in the world did I end up here having started life in South East Asia, then Ireland and now Newcastle. However each day our patients, the dedication of the people we work with and in no small measure, the legendary North Eastern spirit of friendliness and welcome makes Newcastle a wonderful place to be.

Just this morning as I prepared for the bronchoscopy list, the patients involved reminded me just how amazingly courageous they are. I constantly remain in awe at the resilience and courage that our patients and their loved ones show in the face of such a difficult process, an often brutally tough recovery period and the uncertainty of the future. They know that the lung transplant may get them some years but the future is unpredictable. Despite all the uncertainties, their positive outlook and determination to make the best of this most unselfish gift of life is inspiring. The term "being a good host" is never a truer statement. I constantly reflect that so many people who have so much more, should be inspired by our patients and their families. More recently I have been tremendously humbled by the generosity of spirit by the families of those that didn't get much time out of their transplant experience. Despite their experience, these families have been so willing to give up time and effort on their own initiative to raise funds and positive publicity for our unit. There are so many of you who want to give back to the unit and to future transplant patients. I can only offer my most humble thanks to all our patients and families.

It is people like you that make people like us, do what we do. The journey continues.

Thank you for giving me a chance to express my reflections and my thanks to all of you.

I remain in awe at the courage of our patients and their families.

The Freeman Heart and Lung Sports Team

Vicky Pettersen

Freeman Sports Team Manager (Adults)

The Freeman sports team takes part in The British Transplant Games annually, each games being held in a different town/city every year in the United Kingdom.

In 2015 the games were in Newcastle & Gateshead. We had 68 competitors taking part in the games at Newcastle. As it was our home games it was a very big year for us. 27 new members joined the team this year, some of whom had only had a transplant in the last 6-12 months.

850 transplant competitors took part altogether from all over Great Britain.

There are also lots of different much smaller Transplant Sport events taking place all through the year where you can have a taster in a particular sport, for example volleyball, racquets/table tennis weekends to name a few.

See the website for most recent details www.fhlta.org.uk

Who can take part?
Anyone can take part in the games/events once they are more than 6 months post-transplant. You do not have to be an athlete. We have people of all abilities in our team. Some people have never taken part in sports until they joined the team.

The Freeman Sports Team at the 2015 British Transplant Games.

What can I take part in?
You can compete in any of the events as long as your doctor thinks you are physically fit enough to take part.

Everyone is required to get a medical form signed from their Transplant Consultant before they are able to take part.

You can enter events as a beginner so don't feel you need to be at a particular standard.

What events are at the games?
A massive range of sports are available. As well as track and field events you can also take part in swimming, cycling, walking, volleyball, fishing, golf, archery, snooker, ten pin bowling, racquets, bowls, darts and walking. You can also do 5-a-side football.

Each competitor can enter a maximum of 5 events.

Donor Run/Mini Marathon 3k/5k Run/Walk
The Donor event is a great event to take part in with family members as your first event at the games.

You can run or walk, or a bit of both, depending on your ability or which you want to do but the best thing about this event is your family can join you by also competing in this event.

All participants get a commemorative medal to take home.

No matter which sport you take up or which event you attend the main emphasis is on celebrating life, enjoying sport and having fun no matter what your ability is.

The other bonus of taking part in the transplant games is that it keeps you fit; lots of our athletes train leading up to the event they enter in, to be the best they can be to honour their donor. So if you take part in different events throughout the year, it means you are keeping fit all year round, which can really benefit your physical and emotional wellbeing.

Please look out for our next events and keep up to date on the clinic notice board and website.

Participants of the 3km walking event.

Some of our new participants have taken the time to write down their thoughts of their first experience of Transplant Games:

"Entering these events were all very personal goals, especially the running, cycling and swimming. Taking part in each of these events was amazing and quite emotional as I had given up hope almost 2 years previous. The donor 3k run was very special as I ran it with my 9 year old daughter and the atmosphere at the quayside was fantastic."

Louise McLellan – Heart transplant 22 months ago.

"Newcastle and Gateshead was my first ever Transplant Games and I can assure you all that it will not be my last. Me, Susan, my sister and friends were there the full 4 days of competition and what an experience it was. I entered the full 5 events but won nought but had the most fantastic time doing it. The donor walk was a very special day, getting to honour my donor was truly inspirational and to do it with my sister just made it even more special".

John Docherty – Double Lung transplant nearly 3 years.

"The first impressions given when I arrived were fantastic. It could have been my nerves, but I felt that the atmosphere was buzzing, my partner and I took to spotting other competitors around the hotel as we checked in. I was signed up to race in the 5K and 10K cycling events around Leazes Park. I didn't place anywhere in the 5K and 10K races, but I managed to push myself harder than ever before, and this has given me the drive to train further to make myself a better cyclist for the next games. However, for me, this wasn't what the games was about. I met other transplantees and made some brilliant friends that I look forward to meeting again soon".

Job Davies – heart transplants 2003 and 2008, cancer survivor 2005-6.

"This was my first games I had no idea how big this event was. I entered all 5 events and didn't manage to win any medals this time. Both myself and my family really enjoyed all 4 days. The highlights for me were the donor run, I didn't realise how emotional it would be with all the very young children taking part. Will definitely be back next year with the gold in the javelin my target".

Alan Wheeldon – Double Lung Transplant, December 2014.

European Heart & Lung Championships

The European Championships is a Bi Annual event. Only Heart and Lung Transplant recipients compete against each other.

In 2014 the championships were in Vilnius, Lithuania.

In 2016 they are in Helsinki, Finland.

When you take part in these Championships you are part of Team GB

Freeman Heart & Lung Children's Team

Michelle Saunders

Freeman Sports Team Manager (Childrens)

As well as an adult's team, The Freeman Hospital also sends a team of children to The British Transplant Games each year.

At the 2015 games, The Freeman Children's Transplant Team received The Best Children's Heart and Lung Team Trophy. The children competed in swimming, cycling, ball throw, table tennis, archery and many more events.

Being able to take part in events like these give the children the confidence to lead full and active lives following their transplants, as well as demonstrating the importance of Organ Donation.

The Freeman children's team receiving the 'Best Heart & Lung Team Trophy.'

Freeman Heart and Lung Transplant Association

Joan Whitney

FHLTA Committee Member

All Heart & Lung Transplant recipients are members of the Freeman Heart & Lung Transplant Association.

The aims of the FHLTA is to support our members following their Heart or Lung Transplant, by providing;

- Advice (if required) on any matter relating to transplantation.

- Specific financial assistance, for the purchase of medical equipment and / or facilities for recreation with a view to improve the patient's life.

- Help with travel to and from hospital appointments.

- Financial support for our team competitors to attend the World, European and British Transplant Games and also other satellite events throughout the year.

- Funding for medical / nursing staff to attend International Conferences which is to the benefit of patients now and in the future.

- Accommodation (and servicing of) for transplant patients and their families to stay in when attending clinic appointments at The Freeman.

One of the aims of the FHLTA is to fund members to attend sporting events, to promote fitness following their transplant and at the same time promoting organ donation which is a very important part of The FHLTA's aims.

NHS Organ Donor Register:
0300 123 23 23
www.organdonation.nhs.uk

Acknowledgements

First of all, I would like to thank everyone who has contributed to the content of this book by writing their story, poem or article, to give their personal account of what transplant means to them.

It's not an easy task putting these emotional, life changing experiences into words and I think everyone has approached the task with heartfelt passion and thoughtfulness.

The overall message I get from reading through every piece is the overwhelming respect and gratitude towards all the Organ Donors and their living relatives. Each and every Donor and their Family are regarded by every heart and every lung recipient as the bravest, the most generous and the kindest people to walk this Earth.

How the decision is made to donate the organs of their beloved relatives, at the time of such sorrow and pain in the knowledge that they need to make a choice while saying their last goodbyes is something you can never comprehend unless you are in that position.

The courage to give someone, a stranger, a second chance at life, is unfathomable.

The transplant patients are a living reminder that they all embrace life and live it to the full. In their own words; which I have heard said dozens of times, "I wouldn't be here if it wasn't for my Donor and their Family."

This book is published to draw awareness to Organ Donation and to hopefully attract people to sign up to The Organ Donation Register and to tell their relatives of their decision.

A big thank you to my son, Dr Richard Caulkin for helping enormously with the editing of this book and for adding all the photos into the stories for me, I would never have got through it all in time without his help.

Thanks to Vicky Pettersen for endlessly contacting Freeman patients and for proof reading the stories. Also,I am very grateful to Wendy for spending her time proof reading my written contributions to this book. For the final proof reading; thank you to both Richard and Wendy for helping me to make sure all the details and grammar are as accurately portrayed as possible.

Gratitude has to be given to our printer/publisher David Exley who has approached the idea of this book with great enthusiasm and supported us right from the beginning of its production, I could recommend him to anyone, thank you David.

I would like to thank The Freeman Heart & Lung Transplant Association for the sponsorship of this book without which I would be trying to raise the money to fund it over a very long time.

Lastly, even though everyone with a connection to The Freeman was welcomed to contribute to this book, I would like to acknowledge the patients and /or families of patients who felt it was far too emotional a task to write their own or their relative's story.

My heart goes out to you.

Judith Caulkin

Copyright of photos: credit is written next to each photo in each individual story where they are printed. We are very grateful for the kind permission to use photos listed below:

Permission courtesy of;

Donald Fraser, Highland News (photo of Anne MacLennan)
Rob Wilson (Kaylee Olly photo of her as a baby in hospital)
Pete Berry, Sunderland Echo (Kaylee at Tyne Bridge)
Alec Finlay (Artist who designed the Taigh at The Memorial in Scotland)
Hannah Devereux (Photographer of the Taigh for the pamphlet)
National Memorial for Organ and Tissue Donors Pamphlet courtesy of The Scottish Government.

Freeman Hospital, Newcastle-upon-Tyne

INSTITUTE OF TRANSPLANTATION

WE HEAL AND TEACH

"Jack's life was saved by someone we never even met."

Organ donation.
Speak up and save a life.
To find out more go to
organdonationni.info

HSC Public Health Agency   DHSSPS

Register to join the NHS Organ Donor Register today

It takes less than 2 minutes

Age and existing medical conditions are not a barrier –
Anyone can join

Online: www.organdonation.nhs.uk

Phone: 0300 123 23 23

Most importantly, discuss your wishes with your family and
friends

Notes